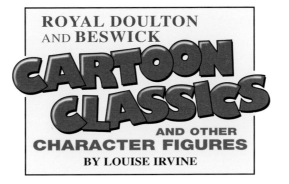

ROYAL DOULTON
AND BESWICK

CARTOON CLASSICS

AND OTHER
CHARACTER FIGURES

BY LOUISE IRVINE

Design by Bill King, King Design and Print, Ipswich, Suffolk, England

Photography by Mark Ward of Elm Studio and Gerald Wells of Northern Counties Photographers

Phototypesetting by Winsor Clarke Typesetting, Ipswich, Suffolk, England

Film Origination by Leverpress Ltd, Ipswich, Suffolk, England

Printed in Great Britain by Leverpress Ltd, Ipswich, Suffolk, England

Binding by J W Braithwaite and Son Limited

Published and distributed by UK International Ceramics Ltd,
10 Wilford Bridge Spur, Melton, Woodbridge, Suffolk IP12 1RJ, England

ISBN 0 9517772 7 0

FIRST PUBLISHED IN GREAT BRITAIN 1998

ROYAL DOULTON
AND BESWICK

CARTOON CLASSICS

AND OTHER

CHARACTER FIGURES

BY LOUISE IRVINE

ACKNOWLEDGEMENTS

I SHOULD like to thank everybody who has been involved in the the production of this book, especially Bill Buckley, Bob and Irene Davidge, Derek and Jean Garrod, Philip and Robin Riley, Jean Thornton, Tom Power and Ann Wheeler, who loaned pieces from their collections for photography. Several keen collectors have also provided information and photographs of rare pieces, including Paul Babb, Kathy and Glyn Gilbert, Dr Steven Ross, Marilyn Sweet and Glynis Motyer.

I am grateful to all the Royal Doulton personnel who assisted me in my research, notably Valerie Baynton, Kevin Bennett, Chris Bott, Alexander Clement, Mike Graham, Richard Halliday, Amanda Hughes-Lubeck, Julie McKeown, Mary Moorcroft and Paula Pointon. I am also indebted to Harry Sales, Peter Roberts and Graham Tongue for providing much valuable material about their work for the Beswick studios.

The licensing agents who represent the featured products have also been very helpful, in particular the Copyrights Group Ltd, Copyright Promotions, Enid Blyton Ltd and Turner Entertainment Ltd.

Special thanks also to Ian Howe for writing a chapter of this book and supplying details about current Royal Doulton products and to Harvey May for providing information and reviewing the Beswick listings. Maureen Batkin was also very generous with information about children's ware by other manufacturers.

Additional photographs were kindly supplied by Jean Dale, Jocelyn Lukins, the British Film Institute, Wendy Wort of Richard Dennis Publications, Mark Wilkinson of Christie's and Mark Oliver of Phillips Auctioneers.

Finally, I should like to thank Nick Tzimas for making this book possible, my husband George for reading the manuscript and giving me so much advice and support and my son Ben for keeping me up to date with all the cartoon characters of today.

LOUISE IRVINE

HOW TO USE THIS BOOK

THE CARTOON classics and other characters featured in this book are arranged chronologically according to their production dates at the Royal Doulton and Beswick factories. Thus Bonzo, which was Royal Doulton's first cartoon character in the 1920s, is discussed in Chapter 1 and the Wizard of Oz series, the most recent commission, is at the end of the book, Chapter 24. The exception to this is the Walt Disney section, Chapter 5, where old and new series are grouped together. The contents page gives the precise location of each series.

Production dates and model numbers are given in the captions to the illustrations but at the end of each chapter there are more details on each character listed in model number order. Chapter 27 features a rarity guide by Nick Tzimas and here the figures are arranged alphabetically by series. There is also an alphabetical index on pages 190-194 to help you locate individual pieces. We hope you enjoy this book.

Contents

Introduction

W̶ALT DISNEY was once asked the secret of his success and he responded 'Every one of us was once a child. We grow up, our personalities change, but within every one of us something remains of our childhood... In planning a picture we don't think of grown-ups and we don't think of children, but just of that fine, clean unspoiled spot down deep in every one of us...' As a result, generations of children and adults have shared the magic of Disney cartoons and spin-off collectables.

Over the years, many other successful animators and authors have discovered this special 'spot', creating classic characters that have left a lasting impression in our lives. They create a nostalgic link with our youth and, in some cases, fond memories are revived by the arrival of children and grandchildren. This is a time when favourite bedtime stories are re-read and cartoons dominate TV viewing. Nurseries are decorated with wallpaper, fabrics, toys and china figures featuring storybook and film characters and the most cherished ornaments often inspire serious collections.

Around the world there are many dedicated collectors of Mickey Mouse, Bonzo and Rupert Bear memorabilia, to name just a few of the most famous characters. Some collectors seek out portraits of their heroes in lots of different media whilst others specialise. Ceramic figures are amongst the most popular collectables and Royal Doulton, John Beswick and Royal Albert are some of the best known brands.

Royal Doulton

The Royal Doulton factory was established in London in 1815 and began the production of art pottery in the 1870s. Humorous characters from classic tales were amongst the earliest figurative works produced at their Lambeth factory. George Tinworth, their first artist, enjoyed modelling stoneware figures of comical animals engaged in human activities, some of which were inspired by Aesop's fables. His assistant Mark Marshall made paperweights fashioned after characters from *Alice's Adventures in Wonderland* whilst Francis Pope portrayed Mr Toad from *The Wind in the Willows* in different guises.

Mr Toad stoneware figure modelled by Francis Pope, c1910

1

The majority of Royal Doulton figures, however, were made at their factory in Burslem, Stoke-on-Trent which was added to the company in 1877. Their celebrated Art Director, Charles Noke, introduced the famous HN range of figures in 1913 and continued the tradition of modelling amusing animals with human attributes. His *Pedlar Wolf* (HN5) was derived from a fable by La Fontaine whilst his *Granny Owl* (HN173) and *Huntsman Fox* (HN100) inhabit a similar fantasy world.

Huntsman Fox and Granny Owl modelled by Charles Noke, 1918

Centre left: Gibson Girl plate, 1901

Below left: Kateroo vase with designs by David Souter, 1906-39

Kateroo model, 1918-28

Cartoons

As well as being a talented figure modeller, Noke was also expert at adapting the graphic styles of contemporary cartoons for his Series ware range, an assortment of ornamental and practical items printed with popular imagery. The word 'cartoon' was first used by *Punch* magazine in 1843 to describe the new full page illustrations which featured in their witty periodical and it was not until the 20th century that it came to mean any comic drawing or animated film.

In 1901, Noke received permission to reproduce some cartoons from *Life* magazine drawn by the successful New York artist, Charles Dana Gibson. His 'Gibson Girl' was used to comment on the social life of the time and the archetypal Edwardian beauty rapidly became a cult figure, appearing on a wide range of merchandise including Royal Doulton plates and vases. These successful designs were followed in 1906 by a series featuring the *Kateroo* cartoons created by David Henry Souter for the *Sydney Bulletin*. Plates and various other shapes were decorated with these art nouveau style drawings and in 1918 the series was extended to include a large figurative portrait of the quarrelsome *Kateroo* (HN154), the first Royal Doulton model to be based on a cartoon character.

Introduction

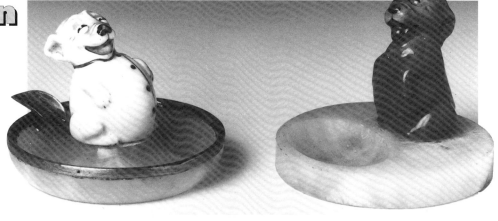

Right: Ashtrays with Bonzo models, 1922-36

Below: Series ware with cartoon characters: Kateroo plate; Gibson Girl vase; Bateman tray, Aldin plate and Bateman box, 1901-40

A few years later, *Bonzo* the famous cartoon dog of the 1920s joined the Royal Doulton HN collection, together with *Ooloo*, his feline companion. *Bonzo* raised laughs regularly in *The Sketch* magazine, on postcard designs and in product advertisements and then went on to appear in some of the earliest British animated cartoons so he can claim to be the first film star in the Royal Doulton collection. Dog lovers will also be familiar with the work of Cecil Aldin whose drawings of mischievous dogs enlivened many magazine illustrations and advertisements in the early 1900s. A range of *Aldin ware* was introduced by Royal Doulton in the mid 1920s and a decade later his playful pups inspired a delightful collection of models entitled *Dogs of Character.*

Below: Advertisement for Aldin's Dogs Series ware, 1926

ROYAL DOULTON
"Aldin's Dogs."

CECIL ALDIN is the acknowledged Master in the drawing of the comic dog, and in this series a number of his clever studies are adapted to a full line of interesting and useful articles. The general effect is bold and decorative and each piece bears the artist's signature.

ROYAL DOULTON POTTERIES
Burslem, Stoke-on-Trent
England

A list is given overleaf of the articles that can be supplied.

Children's Comics

The first cartoons were originally intended for adult enjoyment, although children also responded to the antics of *Bonzo*. Special periodicals had been produced for the amusement of children since the 1860s and were known disparagingly as 'Penny Dreadfuls' in the UK and 'Dime Novels' in the US. Despite widespread condemnation of their sensational style, there was a huge readership for these cheap papers, particularly amongst families who could not afford the new children's books. *Alice's Adventures in Wonderland* (1865), for example, cost around a third of a workman's average weekly wage.

Most of the early children's periodicals consisted of adventure stories with occasional illustrations but gradually the cartoon and comic strip began to appear and the standard features of today's comics, including the full-page humorous strip, speech balloons, regular characters and colour printing, were all established by the turn of the century. Two of the most popular children's comics in the UK made their debut in the 1930s and they are still going strong today. *The Dandy,* which appeared in

1937, introduced a larger than life personality with extraordinary strength called *Desperate Dan.* In 1995 he was portrayed as a Royal Doulton character jug together with *Dennis the Menace,* a leading light of the companion comic, *The Beano.* Their success prompted two other Beano stars in 1996, *Minnie the Minx,* a female version of Dennis, and *Plug* from the *Bash Street Kids.*

*Alice HN2158
modelled by Peggy Davies, 1960-81*

Left: Dennis with Gnasher and Desperate Dan character jugs, 1996-C

Below: Detail of book 'Alice's Adventures in Wonderland'

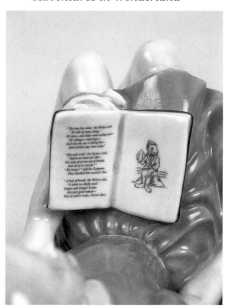

Comic Strips

In the USA, children's comic strips have also been a feature of adult newspapers since the 1890s and the trend began in the UK with the adventures of *Teddy Tail* in the *Daily Mail* (1915). The success of this little mouse became an important element in the circulation war and other newspapers soon followed with their own characters, mostly humanized animals.

Since ancient times, authors and illustrators have used animals acting and conversing in human fashion to amuse and enlighten their readers. Anthropomorphic characters played an important role in many Victorian and Edwardian children's classics, notably *Alice's Adventures in Wonderland* and *The Wind in the Willows.* Their emergence in children's comic strips was a natural

Introduction

Right: Pip, Squeak and Wilfred tray HN935, 1927-36

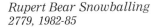

progression and later they became the chief protagonists in animated films.

In 1919 the *Daily Mirror* newspaper introduced *Pip, Squeak and Wilfred,* a dog, a penguin and a rabbit who soon had their own weekly supplement and fan club. A few years later, Royal Doulton launched a range of Series ware depicting this unlikely trio's exploits and they also appeared in figurative form (HN922 and 935). The most enduring of the British comic strip characters, however, is *Rupert Bear* who has appeared in the *Daily Express* newspaper since 1920. This lovable bear's adventures have continued in his own books, annuals and comics. He has starred in plays, TV shows and cartoon films and he has endorsed more than 50 products ranging from umbrellas to toothbrushes. In 1980 Rupert Bear and his friends joined the John Beswick range of character figures.

Rupert Bear Snowballing 2779, 1982-85

John Beswick

The John Beswick factory was established in Longton, Stoke-on-Trent in 1894 to produce affordable tableware and ornaments for the Victorian home. By the 1930s the Beswick artists had begun to specialise in animal modelling and their finely detailed portraits of famous racehorses and champion dogs were soon acclaimed as the best in the industry. At the same time, they demonstrated their whimsical sense of humour with comical studies of animals, often with human expressions and poses. In 1948, the chief modeller, Arthur Gredington, produced a range of figures inspired by the tales of Beatrix Potter and their immediate success led to the introduction of many other appealing subjects from children's literature and animated cartoons.

Animated Cartoons

Most of the early animators were newspaper cartoonists and they introduced their new medium as a screen equivalent of the comic strip, produced with the same regularity. Gradually production became more sophisticated and animated characters with strong personalities began to emerge. The first great cartoon star was

Felix the Cat, who careered through several hundred silent adventures but did not survive the transition to sound.

It was Walt Disney who pioneered the use of synchronised sound in animated films and, in so doing, created the world's most famous cartoon star. *Mickey Mouse* began life as a fairly commonplace rodent called Mortimer but apparently Mrs Disney did not like the name. Initially his antics were quite risqué and violent but his behaviour was modified as he became more famous and supporting characters, such as *Minnie Mouse, Pluto, Goofy* and *Donald Duck,* all helped to enhance the short plots.

Disney's innovations continued to change the course of cartoon production in the 1930s with the introduction of technicolour and the development of the cartoon feature film, beginning with the classic *Snow White and the Seven Dwarfs* in 1938 and continuing with other favourites such as *Pinocchio* (1940) and *Peter Pan* (1952). All of these feature films and the Mickey Mouse shorts provided characters for a series of 20 Disney figures modelled by Arthur Gredington and Jan Granoska at the Beswick factory in the mid 1950s.

One of Disney's top animators, David Hand, moved to England in 1944, tempted by an offer from the Rank Film Organisation to revive the British cartoon industry. He enjoyed some initial success with his *Animaland* series, starring *Zimmy the Lion,* which was launched in 1948, and the following year the Beswick factory produced eight figures of the leading characters, modelled by Arthur Gredington. Financial problems soon closed the short-lived British animation studio, sadly no rival for the celebrated Disney company, which continued to go from strength to strength.

Catalogue page of Disney characters, 1954

Introduction

*Winnie the Pooh 2193,
1969-89*

*Right: Lord of the Rings
fotonovel, 1979*

In the 1960s Disney enjoyed considerable success with their interpretation of the *Winnie the Pooh* stories written by A.A. Milne some forty years earlier. The 'Bear of Little Brain' quickly became a popular merchandising character and the Beswick factory secured the rights to introduce a collection of eight characters from the mini cartoon features in 1969. This was the year the company was taken over by the Royal Doulton group as the Beswick family had no heirs for their thriving business. Royal Doulton transferred production of many of their famous ranges to the newly acquired factory and the two design studios have worked closely together ever since. Often models, which were designed and produced at Beswick, have been given a Royal Doulton backstamp, for example the second collection of *Winnie the Pooh* figures introduced in 1996.

Recently Royal Doulton have also been working with Disney on the *Princess* collection. These large size figures for the HN range were designed by Pauline Parsons and feature heroines from some of the classic feature films, such as *Cinderella* (1950) as well as more recent productions, such as *The Little Mermaid* (1989) and *Beauty and the Beast* (1991).

The cost of making Disney style cartoon features eventually became prohibitive for most film producers and alternatives were sought. A cartoon version of Tolkien's fantasy *The Lord of the Rings* was produced by Saul Zaentz in 1978 and combined traditional animation techniques with rotoscoping, which uses live action footage. Royal Doulton were offered the opportunity to link with this film by creating a collection of figures based on Tolkien's mythological characters and Design Manager, Harry Sales, was given the task of interpreting these bizarre beings.

Expansion and Development

From the 1960s to the mid 1980s, Harry Sales designed most of the character figures to emerge from the Beswick kilns. This was an exciting period of expansion and development as the Beswick factory was taken over by the Royal Doulton group in 1969. Five years earlier, Royal Doulton had also acquired the Royal Albert factory, which is renowned for bone china tableware, particularly *Old Country Roses,* acclaimed as the world's best selling china pattern. Appropriate brand names from the group's portfolio are now chosen for marketing and distribution reasons, thus figures made at the Beswick factory can have a Royal Doulton, Royal Albert or John Beswick backstamp. For example, the figures inspired by Kenneth Grahame's classic *The Wind in the Willows* were given a Royal Albert backstamp, whilst the *Alice in Wonderland* collection had a John Beswick backstamp.

Children's Books

Many of the subjects designed by Harry Sales were suggested by best selling children's books, whether it be established classics or contemporary publications, such as A *Friend is Someone who Likes You* by Joan Walsh Anglund, which inspired a group of Beswick figures in 1969. Whenever possible, Harry liaised closely with the originators of the personalities he portrayed. He spent many happy hours at Norman Thelwell's studio discussing this artist's cartoons for *Angels on Horseback* and he chose several designs for the Beswick collection in 1981. He also visited Epping Forest with Jill Barklem to familiarise himself with the setting for the *Brambly Hedge* stories and he designed most of the Royal Doulton figure collection. Often it was quite a challenge to adapt the book illustrations for the ceramic medium and the soft crayon

Drawing by Norman Thelwell, 1981

drawings for *The Snowman* by Raymond Briggs particularly stretched his ingenuity. The resulting collection of Royal Doulton figures is now very sought after.

Unfortunately, not all of Harry's ideas made it into production. He envisaged a range of figures inspired by Roger Hargreaves' *Mr Men* but they did not progress beyond the drawing board, whilst *Asterix the Gaul* and the *Muppets* were modelled in the mid 1970s but never introduced. With new children's characters, it is often hard to predict their lifespan and consequently some golden opportunities have slipped by.

Mr Greedy design by Harry Sales for a proposed Mr Men series. Not produced

Left: Harry Sales, Jill Barklem and Peter Roberts discussing Brambly Hedge wares, 1982

Introduction

Few literary critics would have believed that the *Noddy* stories, written by Enid Blyton, would remain popular for nearly fifty years, despite being excluded from many public libraries for not being politically correct. However, Miss Blyton remains the most successful children's author this century and Noddy is experiencing a revival with his own magazine and BBC television show. A new wave of character merchandise has been prompted by this high profile, including the Royal Doulton figures of *Noddy, Big Ears, Mr Plod* and *Tessie Bear.*

Paddington Bear, created by Michael Bond in 1955, is another favourite pre-school character who has reached a wider audience through television. Paddington is always getting himself into a muddle and many of his humorous escapades have now been interpreted in minute detail using Royal Doulton's new resin body.

Paddington Bear

TV Cartoons

As well as revitalising established children's characters, television has also introduced many new stars. The pioneers in TV cartoons were William Hanna and Joseph Barbera, who made their reputation with the *Tom & Jerry* cinema shorts for MGM in the 1940s and 50s. More than half a century later, the antics of this feuding cat and mouse team are still as popular on the small screen and, in 1995, UK International Ceramics paid tribute to their continuing success by commissioning limited edition portrait figures from the John Beswick studio.

With the advent of television, Hanna and Barbera realised that the future of cartoons lay in the more economical system of limited animation which required fewer drawings. To compensate for the lack of visual detail, they gave greater importance to the comedy script and the character voices, which gave added life to the cartoon.

Their first great success was *The Flintstones,* an animated situation comedy aimed at adults as well as children. Launched in 1960, it set a record as the longest running TV show in broadcast history and it is still going strong today. Generations of viewers have laughed at life in the Stone Age city of Bedrock, where the Flintstones and their friends, the Rubbles, drive around in foot-powered Flintmobiles, dine

Right: Tom & Jerry

The Flintstones Collection, 1996

out on barbecued bronto-burgers and watch Stony Curtis movies! The seven members of these suburban prehistoric families, including their pet dinosaur, Dino, were immortalised as limited edition John Beswick figures for UK International Ceramics in 1996.

Another very popular Hanna-Barbera show, starring *Top Cat,* was first screened on American TV in 1961. The cartoons follow the raffish adventures of the enterprising TC and his feline gang as they hustle their way through downtown streets and alleys, trying to avoid the clutches of the cop on the beat, Officer Dibble. Over the years, Top Cat has appeared on a variety of character merchandise, including mugs, T shirts and hats, and he was even the spokesman for the Royal Bank of Scotland in an advertising campaign. No doubt he would recommend the limited edition Beswick figure of himself and his alley cohorts as a sound investment!

Top Cat 3581, 1996

Supermarionation

Whilst Hanna-Barbera and other American animators were concentrating on TV cartoons during the 1960s, Gerry and Sylvia Anderson were entertaining British audiences with their Supermarionation shows, starring puppet characters. *Stingray, Captain Scarlet* and *Thunderbirds* are all action packed adventures set in the future and they attracted a huge adult following in addition to their young TV audience. *Thunderbirds,* in particular, achieved cult status and the John Beswick studio marked the 30th anniversary of the series with six limited edition portrait busts of the principal puppet heroes and villains.

The Future

Exciting developments continue in the animation industry with Nick Park's award-winning claymation characters *Wallace and Gromit* and the new computer generated graphics for *Toy Story,* distributed by the Disney corporation. In addition, many classic characters continue to be revived on television so there will be no shortage of candidates for Royal Doulton's cartoon collection in the future. Details of new introductions are eagerly awaited by collectors but for now ... *That's all folks!*

Bonzo and Ooloo

*Above: Ooloo the Cat
HN819, 1923-32*

*Below: Bonzo version 4
HN815, 1922-36*

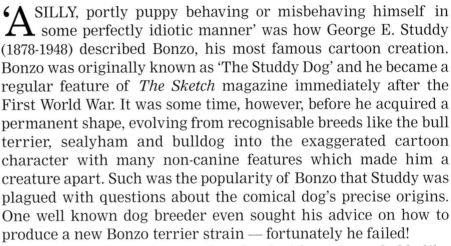

'A SILLY, portly puppy behaving or misbehaving himself in some perfectly idiotic manner' was how George E. Studdy (1878-1948) described Bonzo, his most famous cartoon creation. Bonzo was originally known as 'The Studdy Dog' and he became a regular feature of *The Sketch* magazine immediately after the First World War. It was some time, however, before he acquired a permanent shape, evolving from recognisable breeds like the bull terrier, sealyham and bulldog into the exaggerated cartoon character with many non-canine features which made him a creature apart. Such was the popularity of Bonzo that Studdy was plagued with questions about the comical dog's precise origins. One well known dog breeder even sought his advice on how to produce a new Bonzo terrier strain — fortunately he failed!

Bonzo's cheeky antics struck a chord with young and old alike and, having been officially named in 1922, he went from strength to strength, becoming a weekly fixture in *The Sketch* magazine. Before long his well-known image was being used to endorse such diverse products as collar studs, ladies suspenders, razor blades, quilts and motor cars. A giant Bonzo puffing on a Pinnace cigarette was one of the first neon signs to be put up in Piccadilly Circus in 1924.

Bonzo made his stage debut in 1923, performing in several comedy shows and pantomimes, and the following year he became a star of the silver screen, appearing in 26 animated films which were released fortnightly throughout 1925. The thousands of drawings required for these 8-10 minute cartoons were all drawn by Studdy with a team of assistants and their technical excellence set new standards for the emerging British animation industry. Bonzo's popularity was not confined to Britain and his cartoons were syndicated in India, South Africa, South America and the USA, where he had front cover treatment on *The American Weekly*. The demand for Bonzo's escapades seemed insatiable and it was fortunate that Studdy's motto was 'Work whilst others play'. The fruits of his endeavours ensured an affluent lifestyle for his family in Kensington and he received many accolades for his achievements. One of his greatest honours was the invitation to

paint a tiny portrait of Bonzo to hang in Queen Mary's Doll's House, now at Windsor Castle.

Bonzo's international fame led to lots of spin-off merchandise for adults and children, including velveteen and wooden toys, games, jigsaws, sweet packaging, toiletries, perfume bottles, bridge accessories, ashtrays and china ornaments. Several china manufacturers produced little figures of Bonzo and Royal Doulton introduced five models in several different colourways to their famous HN range in 1922.

The first Royal Doulton model (392) depicts Bonzo lying down and it was issued in cream only as HN804. It has proved to be the hardest of all to find. In the second model (389) Bonzo is sitting up with his mouth wide open and this was made in purple (HN805A), yellow (HN809) and blue (HN811). It has also been found in the rare Chinese Jade glaze which obscures much of the detail. The third model (387) is very similar to the second but the mouth is not opened as wide. It was produced in four colourways, purple (HN805B), cream with black spots (HN808), green (HN810) and orange (HN812). The best known of all the Doulton models (393) shows Bonzo wearing a buttoned jacket and this was made with black buttons (HN814), red buttons (HN815) and red all over (HN826). A fifth model (388) was discovered in 1997 but no

Left: Bonzo Annuals, 1935-52

Above: Advertisement for Stage Guild Ball and Lucky the Cat K12, 1932-75

Below: Ooloo the Cat HN827, 1923-32

Bonzo and Ooloo

HN numbers have been recorded. Several of the seated models of Bonzo can also be found mounted on alabaster ashtrays and they had all been withdrawn by 1936.

Although interest in Bonzo continued throughout the 1930s, with lots of books, annuals and postcards appearing on the market, he was no longer the star of *The Sketch* magazine. Studdy had decided to slow down his canine character's career, feeling it was time for something new. As an artist he had much more to offer and throughout his career he had contributed many different types of illustrations to a wide range of comics and magazines. Animals were always his primary interest, following his early art and anatomy studies at Calderon's Animal School, and he created several engaging characters such as Yop the donkey, Bill the terrier, Tony the mouse and Ooloo the cat.

Ooloo was the only one of Studdy's comical creatures to share the limelight with Bonzo. She developed from being the victim of the pup's practical jokes to become his fellow conspirator until, by 1929, this 'new load of mischief' had her own cartoons in *The Sketch* and *The Humorist* magazines. Soft toys and ceramic models of Ooloo began to appear on the shop shelves beside Bonzo. The Royal Doulton archives record a model of Ooloo (400) in the HN range as early as 1923. Five different colourways are listed (HN818, 819, 827, 828 and 829) but only a couple of these early decorations have come to light. However, the model was re-numbered K12 in 1932 and continued in production until 1975. Today this little black cat model is known to most collectors as 'Lucky'.

BONZO GETS THAT SPRING FEELING.
The reason for Bonzo's Spring feeling is obvious. Chee-Kee takes the easy way.
[Drawn by G. E. Studdy.

Illustration from the Sketch Magazine, 1923

Bonzo and Ooloo

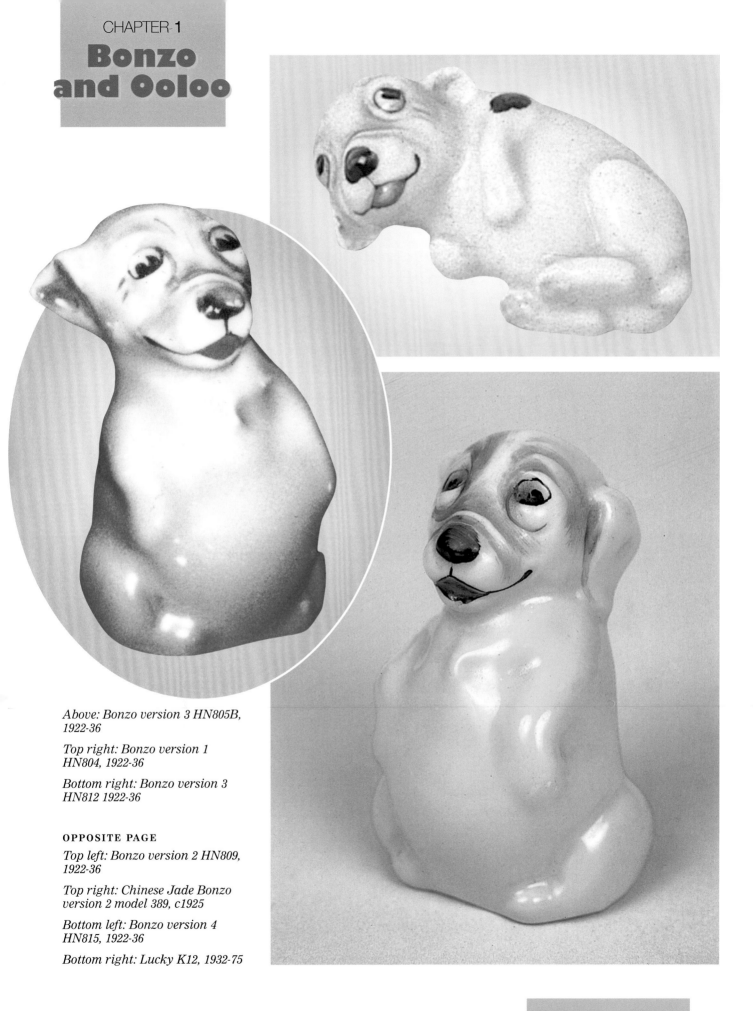

Above: Bonzo version 3 HN805B, 1922-36

Top right: Bonzo version 1 HN804, 1922-36

Bottom right: Bonzo version 3 HN812 1922-36

OPPOSITE PAGE

Top left: Bonzo version 2 HN809, 1922-36

Top right: Chinese Jade Bonzo version 2 model 389, c1925

Bottom left: Bonzo version 4 HN815, 1922-36

Bottom right: Lucky K12, 1932-75

Bonzo and Ooloo

BONZO AND OOLOO

Royal Doulton backstamp
Designed by George Studdy

Bonzo in five models and various colourways
Introduced: 1922   Withdrawn: 1936

Bonzo lying down
Version 1, model 392
Height: 1 inch 2.5 cm
HN804   cream

Bonzo sitting with mouth wide open
Version 2, model 389
Height: 2 inches 5 cm
HN805A purple/blue
HN809   yellow
HN811   blue
                 Chinese Jade

Bonzo sitting with mouth open a little
Version 3, model 387
Height: 2 inches 5 cm
HN805B purple/blue
HN808   cream with black spots
HN810   green
HN812   orange/yellow

Bonzo wearing a buttoned jacket
Version 4, model 393
Height: 2 inches 5 cm
HN814   black buttons
HN815   red buttons
HN826   red

Bonzo with head leaning back
Version 5, model 388
Height: 1¹/₂ inches 3 cm
No HN numbers recorded

Ooloo the cat (Lucky)
Model 400 in various colourways
Introduced: 1923 Withdrawn: c1932
HN818   black with white face
HN819   white
HN827   ginger
HN828   tabby
HN829   black and white
K12   (1932 – 1975)
                 black with white face

Top: Bonzo version 3 HN808, 1922-36

Bottom: Bonzo version 5, model 388, 1922-36

Pip, Squeak & Wilfred

PIP THE DOG, Squeak the penguin and Wilfred the rabbit had starring roles in a strip cartoon which ran in the children's section of the Daily Mirror newspaper from 1919 until 1955. The anthropomorphic trio was the idea of Bertram J Lamb who was known to the young readers as Uncle Dick but it was cartoonist Austen Bowen Payne who visualised their adventures. Payne was a well known black and white artist of the period and contributed to many children's comics, for example *Firefly, Illustrated Chips* and *Tiger Tim's Weekly.* However, Pip, Squeak and Wilfred took up most of his time and, during the first three years of the pets' existence, he turned out well over two thousand drawings. He took his first day off in 1922 and on that occasion the cartoon was drawn by his understudy, H F Pothecary.

Such was the popularity of Pip, Squeak and Wilfred that, by 1921, they had appeared in their own supplement to the *Daily Mirror,* entitled *Pip and Squeak* which was given free every Saturday until 1925. By that time they also had their own Annual which had been launched in 1923 and which ran for many years incorporating the twin publication *Wilfred's Annual* in 1938. Mr Payne loved drawing Wilfred best and admitted in 1922 that 'The little rabbit now even overshadows the penguin and the dog. I can't keep him in the background — he must be in the limelight all the time!'

Fans of the mischievous trio could join the Wilfredian League of Gugnuncs, so called because 'Gug' and 'Nunc' for Uncle were amongst the few words which young Wilfred could utter. Members raised many thousands of pounds for charity and a 1928 rally at the Royal Albert Hall was attended by nearly 90,000 people, with children yelling their secret password 'Ick Ick Pah Boo'.

It was no doubt with young league members in mind that Royal Doulton first produced their Pip, Squeak and Wilfred ware. A tray featuring Pip, Squeak and Wilfred (HN935) was modelled at the Burslem studio in 1927 along with a figure of Wilfred blowing a trumpet (HN922) and they remained in the range until 1936. Five different cartoons have been recorded on mugs, cups, saucers and tea plates also dating from 1927. The first

*Pip, Squeak and Wilfred
tray HN935, 1927-36*

shows Pip, Squeak and Wilfred in procession behind a young boy carrying the banner of the Wilfredian League of Gugnuncs, symbolised by a pair of rabbit's ears and the initials WLOG. The other scenes also feature the famous threesome in various pursuits with the exception of one which depicts two different characters, Squeak's aged 'Auntie' and 'Popski' the dog, who are being asked if they are 'Going to join the Gugnuncs'. It is possible to find all the scenes printed in either sepia, blue or green outline, as well as brightly coloured, and the latter style has most appeal to collectors today. According to the pattern books, the Lambeth studio also produced a mug (X8663) featuring the trio modelled in relief but, judging from its rarity today, it could not have been made in any quantity.

The trio appeared in many guises besides china, for example on greeting cards and as chocolate models. In 1936 they made their screen debut in a six minute programme about the artist A B Payne, by then sixty years of age. He was featured at work

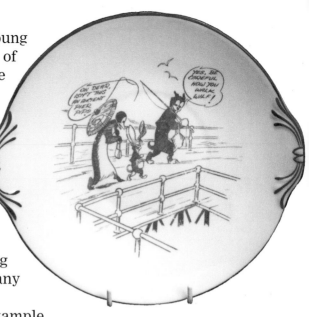

Pip, Squeak and Wilfred plate with scene 5 in sepia, 1927-35

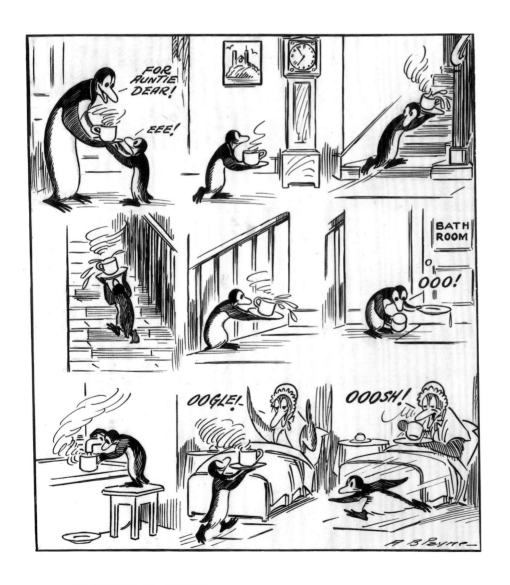

Page from Pip, Squeak and Wilfred Annual, 1926

Pip, Squeak & Wilfred

Right: Pip and Squeak Annual, 1926

Pip, Squeak and Wilfred mug with scene 1, 1927-35

Below: Pip, Squeak and Wilfred mug with scene 4, baby plate with scene 2 and plate with scene 3, 1927-35

wearing a hooded gown printed all over with silhouettes of Squeak and, as he drew, he was surrounded by all sorts of mechanical Pips, Squeaks and Wilfreds, larger than life! This film fantasy increased the pets' popularity, which continued through the war years, even though cartoons did not appear in the *Daily Mirror* due to the paper shortage. Their exploits were revived in 1947 and continued until 1955. Four years later Austen Payne died and his obituary confirmed the widespread popularity of his cartoons. 'Letters applauding the antics of Pip, Squeak and Wilfred came from bishops, politicians, industrialists and authors and, on one occasion, a Speaker of the House of Commons sent them an anniversary greeting in rhyme'. Fortunately the unlikely friends will live on indefinitely on Doulton wares as these cups and saucers will no longer be given to baby to bash up and down on the high chair!

Pip, Squeak and Wilfred tray HN935 and plate with scene 5 in polychrome, 1927-35

20

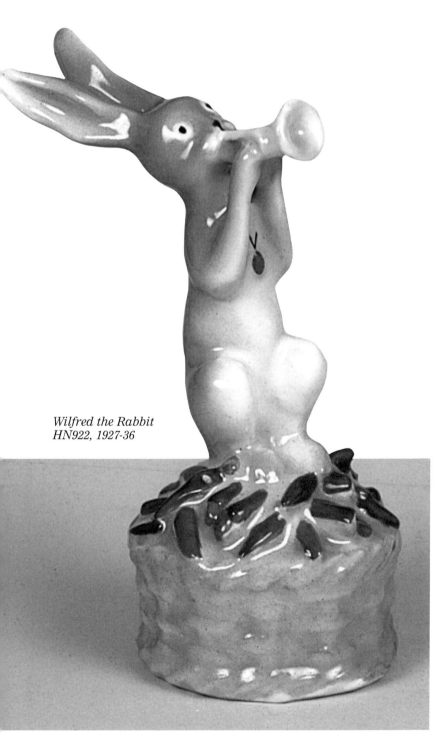

*Wilfred the Rabbit
HN922, 1927-36*

PIP, SQUEAK AND WILFRED

Royal Doulton backstamp
Designed by A B Payne for *The Daily Mirror*
newspaper

HN922 Wilfred the Rabbit
Height: 4 inches 10 cm
Introduced: 1927   Withdrawn: 1936

HN935 Pip, Squeak and Wilfred on Tray
Height: 4 inches 10 cm
Introduced: 1927   Withdrawn: 1936

PIP, SQUEAK AND WILFRED NURSERY WARE

Royal Doulton backstamp
Produced from 1927 to 1935
Designed by A B Payne for *The Daily Mirror*

Scenes
1 'We sing this song for we all belong'
  — Squeak and Pip

2 'Goodbye Dear. I hope you find them at
  home' — Squeak
  'So long Wilf! Be back to lunch' — Pip

3 'What is it Wilfred? Don't hold on to my
  bag like that!' — Squeak
  'Nunc' — Wilf
  'He wants a penny I expect, Squeak' — Pip

4 'Hello Popski and Auntie going to join the
  Gugnuncs?' — Gook Nooski
  'Mmm' — Auntie

5 'Oh Dear isn't this an ancient pier Pip'
  — Squeak
  'Yes, Be careful where you walk Wilf' —
  Pip

Shapes
Plates 6 inch, baby plate, mug, cups and
saucers

Pattern numbers
D4692, D4741, D4752, D4753, H3485

M I Hummel

Sister Maria Innocentia Hummel

OPPOSITE PAGE
Shepherd Boy 914, 1941-48

THE OUTBREAK of the Second World War gave an unexpected opportunity to the Beswick Pottery. Without any concern for copyright reprisals, they were able to produce their own versions of the M I Hummel figures, made famous by the Goebel factory in Germany.

These delightful studies of children were based on designs by a young nun, Sister Maria Innocentia Hummel. Her art work was discovered in 1934 by Franz Goebel, the fourth generation owner of the Goebel Porcelain factory, during a visit to a religious art shop in Munich. He purchased some cards, which were reproduced from her original paintings, and studied them with his top modellers Arthur Moller and Reingold Unger. Everybody was charmed by the innocent little children portrayed in Sister Maria's paintings and Goebel sought permission to transform them into ceramic figures.

Goebel visited the Franciscan convent at Seissen, where Sister Maria Innocentia had lived since her graduation from Munich art school in 1931, and an arrangement was reached for royalties to be paid to the Convent. All figures were to be approved before production began and Sister Maria Innocentia occasionally made suggestions about the poses and colours of the figures which were made under her name. She also visited the Goebel factory to meet the modellers and see the figures being made. The first models were shown at the Leipzig Trade Fair in 1935 and were favourably received by American retailers. They sold very well in the US department stores and Goebel soon asked permission to introduce more figures. Each M I Hummel figure was assigned a pattern number which was incised on the base of the figures.

The pastoral innocence of M I Hummel's artwork was a source of joy to many as the storm clouds gathered over Nazi Germany. In 1937, Hitler's government closed all Catholic schools and imposed severe taxes on all convents, difficulties which Seissen survived thanks to the royalties paid by the Goebel firm. By 1939, Americans opposed to the policies of the Nazi regime stopped importing German products, including M I Hummel figures. The war began a few months later and the Goebel factory concentrated on making products for the war effort, including insulators for the communications lines and tableware for the troops.

With Britain and Germany now engaged in a bitter war, the Beswick factory had no qualms about usurping the successful M I Hummel designs and making their own figures for the American market. In 1940, Arthur Gredington modelled twelve of the most popular Goebel subjects, including *Strolling Along* (HUM 5), *Book Worm* (HUM 3) and *Globe Trotter* (HUM 109). Eleven of these figures went into production and are illustrated in a 1942 catalogue — one model of a girl strumming a banjo called Happiness remained in prototype form.

It is not known whether Sister Maria Innocentia knew about these copies. During the war years, she had many more pressing problems to deal with. The convent was closed down, becoming a repatriation centre for Germans returning from abroad. Sister Maria Innocentia cared for the sick but her own health was failing. She suffered several relapses before her condition was finally diagnosed as chronic TB in 1944. She died at the age of 37 in 1946.

When the Iron Curtain was drawn at the end of the war, the Goebel factory was in the American zone, surrounded on three sides by Soviet territory. Production started slowly but, before long, the M I Hummel figures were being made again and were soon avidly collected by GI's and their wives. Their enthusiasm for the cute, wide-eyed children started a trend which has continued to this day.

The Beswick Hummel figures were withdrawn in 1948 and are now as sought after as the originals. What would Sister Maria Innocentia have made of the copies? Perhaps she would echo the words of the famous art potter, William de Morgan, when he was faced with a similar dilemma: 'Imitation is the sincerest form of pottery'.

Puppy Love, left Beswick version, right Hummel version

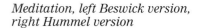

Left: Design for Little Fiddler, Hummel figure 2, 1935

Meditation, left Beswick version, right Hummel version

M I Hummel

Above left: Bugle Boy 903, 1940-48

Above right: Goose Girl 905, 1940-48

Below left: Shepherd Boy 914, 1941-48

Below right: Book Worm 904, 1940-48

Left: Max and Moritz 911, 1941-48

Right: Globe Trotter 913, 1941-48

Above: Stormy Weather 908, 1941-48

Left: Strolling Along 906, 1941-48

Right: Farm Boy 912, 1941-48

26

M I Hummel

M I HUMMEL

John Beswick backstamp

903 Bugle Boy
Hummel 97
Modelled by Arthur Gredington
Height: 4½ inches 11.5 cm
Introduced: 1940   Withdrawn: 1948

904 Book Worm
Hummel 3
Modelled by Arthur Gredington
Height: 5 inches 12.5 cm
Introduced: 1940   Withdrawn: 1948

905 Goose Girl
Hummel 47
Modelled by Arthur Gredington
Height: 6¼ inches 16 cm
Introduced: 1940   Withdrawn: 1948

906 Strolling Along
Hummel 5
Modelled by Arthur Gredington
Height: 4¾ inches 12 cm
Introduced: 1941   Withdrawn: 1948

908 Stormy Weather
Hummel 71
Modelled by Arthur Gredington
Height: 6 inches 15 cm
Introduced: 1941   Withdrawn: 1948

909 Puppy Love
Hummel 1
Modelled by Arthur Gredington
Height: 5¼ inches 13 cm
Introduced: 1941   Withdrawn: 1948

910 Meditation
Hummel 13
Modelled by Arthur Gredington
Height: 5 inches 12.5 cm
Introduced: 1941   Withdrawn: 1948

911 Max and Moritz
Hummel 123
Modelled by Arthur Gredington
Height: 5¾ inches 14.5 cm
Introduced: 1941   Withdrawn: 1948

912 Farm Boy
Hummel 66
Modelled by Arthur Gredington
Height: 6 inches 15 cm
Introduced: 1941   Withdrawn: 1948

913 Globe Trotter
Hummel 109
Modelled by Arthur Gredington
Height: 5 inches 12.5 cm
Introduced: 1941   Withdrawn: 1948

914 Shepherd Boy
Hummel 64
Modelled by Arthur Gredington
Height: 4¾ inches 12 cm
Introduced: 1941   Withdrawn: 1948

990 Happiness
Hummel 86
Modelled by Arthur Gredington
Height: 3 inches 7.5 cm
Prototype model 1942
Not put into production

Puppy Love 909, 1941-48

Meditation 910, 1941-48

David Hand's Animaland

David Hand

OPPOSITE PAGE
Felia 1151, 1950-55

Z IMMY THE LION, Dusty the Mole and Oscar the Ostrich were intended as Britain's answer to Mickey Mouse and Donald Duck but sadly they never captured the public's imagination in the same way. They were developed by David Hand, a distinguished American animator, who came to England in 1944 at the behest of the Rank Film Organisation to set up an animation studio. At that time, J. Arthur Rank, the magnate of the UK film industry, was committed to an exciting programme of research and innovation. He wanted to create a revival of British cartoons that would compete with Hollywood and he wanted to provide much needed employment for ex-servicemen and women.

David Hand's impressive credentials, both as an artist and administrator, suggested he was the ideal man to achieve this. During the 1920s he had worked with the Fleischer brothers on their famous 'Out of the Inkwell' series and then he spent 14 years with Disney animating and directing many of the Mickey Mouse and Silly Symphony cartoons. He was also supervising director for Disney's first cartoon feature *Snow White and the Seven Dwarfs,* launched in 1937, as well as for *Bambi* in 1942.

Hand brought over some of his American colleagues to assist with Rank's new venture, notably Ralph Wright, who created Pluto, and Roy Paterson who had worked on the Tom and Jerry cartoons at MGM. Together they recruited a team of young artists and set up a studio in the sleepy Thames-side village of Cookham. At one time there were over 200 employees at the Gaumont-British Animation Department as the studio was known.

According to David Hand, at least three years were needed to train young artists to animate and they honed their skills working on educational and commercial shorts. There were many teething problems as might be expected with a new venture struggling to succeed in austerity Britain. Some of the more ambitious projects never came to fruition, for example early plans to produce feature length cartoons of Lewis Carroll's *Hunting of the Snark* and Kenneth Grahame's *The Wind in the Willows*. J. Arthur Rank suggested animating well-known characters from the *Daily Mirror* strip cartoons but Hand wanted to create his own original characters.

29

By the end of 1948, Hand's first entertainment cartoons were ready for public viewing and he launched four titles from two different series, *Musical Paintbox* and *Animaland*. The *Musical Paintbox* cartoons were low cost productions set to popular regional tunes with the minimum of animation. The first one, *The Thames,* was quite well received by the critics but later films featuring *Ireland, Wales, Scotland* and some of the English regions were rather dull.

The first *Animaland* cartoons, *The Lion* and *The House Cat,* were criticised for their reliance on a narrator and their similarity to Disney but most critics agreed they lacked the sense of fun and madcap energy of their Hollywood counterparts. New characters helped improve the *Animaland* series, notably the squirrel Ginger Nutt and his girlfriend Hazel, Loopy Hare and Dusty Mole. However, Hand's animators did not have the time to realise their full potential as, by 1949, the Rank Film Organisation faced grave financial difficulties.

Tie-in books and toys were launched to help promote the *Animaland* cartoons, which were shown at Rank's Odeon and Gaumont cinemas and, in 1949, an article appeared in the *Pottery Gazette* recommending Hand's characters as suitable subjects for children's china. Without delay, a Tunstall firm, George Clews and Company, began to produce nursery ware featuring Ginger and

Catalogue page for the Animaland collection, 1950

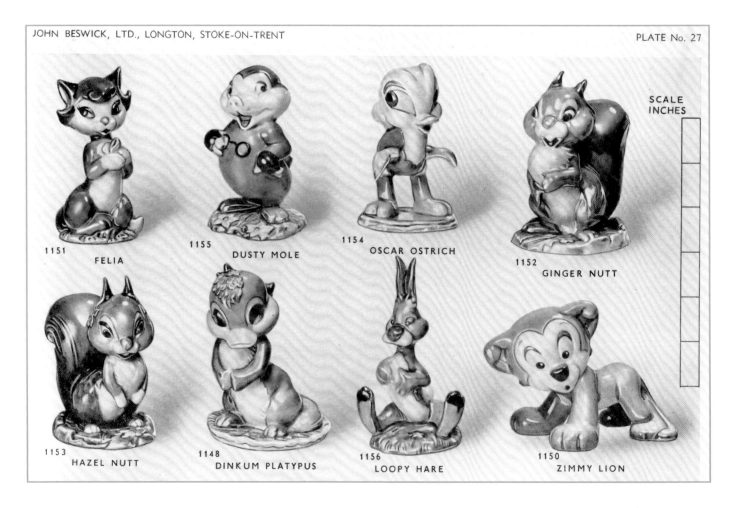

JOHN BESWICK, LTD., LONGTON, STOKE-ON-TRENT

PLATE No. 27

SCALE INCHES

1151 FELIA

1155 DUSTY MOLE

1154 OSCAR OSTRICH

1152 GINGER NUTT

1153 HAZEL NUTT

1148 DINKUM PLATYPUS

1156 LOOPY HARE

1150 ZIMMY LION

David Hand's Animaland

Hazel Nutt and the John Beswick studio produced a range of eight ceramic figures of the leading characters. However, by the time they were on the market in 1950, the Gaumont British Animation Studio had been closed down and David Hand had returned to the USA to pursue a career in industrial films.

Rank's attempt to create a British animation industry to rival Disney, MGM and Warner Brothers had failed. Given the high costs of production, the cartoons could not possibly make money in British cinemas alone, however good, and the Americans were not interested, partly because Hand had poached some of their best animators. Perhaps, if the studio had survived until the mid 1950s, their work might have had a wider audience on television like all the Hanna-Barbera cartoons in the US.

The Beswick *Animaland* figures continued to be produced until 1955 but, judging from the number found in the marketplace today, they could not have sold in great numbers. Ironically, they are now the most sought after of all the cartoon characters in the Beswick collection.

Ginger Nutt promotional sign, c1948

Animaland nursery ware produced by George Clews and Company, c1949

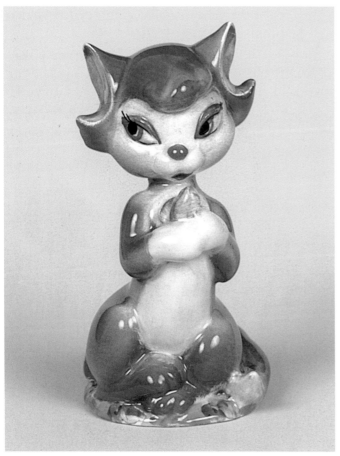

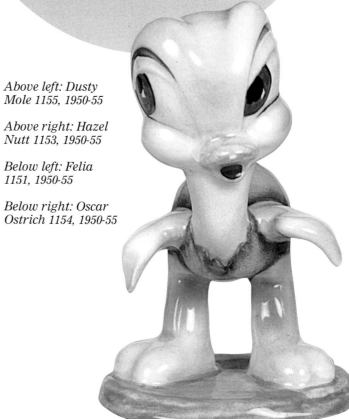

Above left: Dusty Mole 1155, 1950-55

Above right: Hazel Nutt 1153, 1950-55

Below left: Felia 1151, 1950-55

Below right: Oscar Ostrich 1154, 1950-55

David Hand's Animaland

*Left: Zimmy the Lion
1150, 1950-55*

*Right: Dinkum
Platypus 1148, 1950-55*

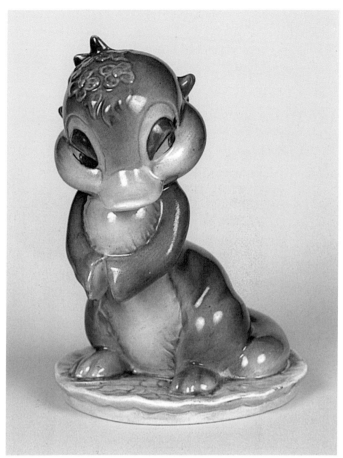

Below left: Ginger Nutt 1152, 1950-55

Below right: Loopy Hare 1156, 1950-55

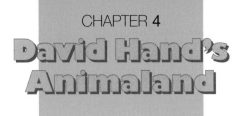

David Hand's Animaland

DAVID HAND'S ANIMALAND

John Beswick backstamp

1148 **Dinkum Platypus**
Modelled by Arthur Gredington
Height: 4¼ inches 10.5 cm
Introduced: 1950   Withdrawn: 1955

1150 **Zimmy the Lion**
Modelled by Arthur Gredington
Height: 3¾ inches 9.5 cm
Introduced: 1950   Withdrawn: 1955

1151 **Felia**
Modelled by Arthur Gredington
Height: 4 inches 10 cm
Introduced: 1950   Withdrawn: 1955

1152 **Ginger Nutt**
Modelled by Arthur Gredington
Height: 4 inches 10 cm
Introduced: 1950   Withdrawn: 1955

1153 **Hazel Nutt**
Modelled by Arthur Gredington
Height: 3¾ inches 9.5 cm
Introduced: 1950   Withdrawn: 1955

1154 **Oscar Ostrich**
Modelled by Arthur Gredington
Height: 3¾ inches 9.5 cm
Introduced: 1950   Withdrawn: 1955

1155 **Dusty Mole**
Modelled by Arthur Gredington
Height: 3½ inches 8.5 cm
Introduced: 1950   Withdrawn: 1955

1156 **Loopy Hare**
Modelled by Arthur Gredington
Height: 4¼ inches 10.5 cm
Introduced: 1950   Withdrawn: 1955

Walt Disney

*Mickey Mouse 1278,
1954-65*

MICKEY MOUSE is the most famous cartoon star in the world, which is not surprising considering all his achievements. He was the first cartoon character to talk, the first to appear in colour and he was a pioneer in the lucrative merchandising business.

Mickey Mouse was the brainchild of Walt Disney, a young cartoonist from Kansas who set up a Hollywood animation studio in 1923. With his brother Roy and several animators, including the talented Ub Iwerks, he launched a successful series of shorts, combining live action with cartoon characters, entitled *Alice in Wonderland* and another featuring the adventures of Oswald the Lucky Rabbit. Problems with Disney's distributor necessitated the creation of a new cartoon character and Mickey Mouse was born. Two cartoons were produced before the revolutionary *Steamboat Willie* was made with synchronised sound in 1929 and Mickey immediately became a national celebrity. Within a year, he had a bigger screen following than most of the stars in Hollywood and his fans ranged from little children to the American President and the British Monarch.

In 1930 a Mickey Mouse Club was launched at cinemas and he made his debut in a daily comic strip. A major merchandising campaign was instigated with the famous mouse endorsing toys, clothes, household goods, stationery, sweets, jewellery and other gift items. Paragon China, now one of the companies within the Royal Doulton group, was the first British pottery to introduce Mickey Mouse nursery ware in 1930. The substantial income from licensed products helped finance the creative development of the Disney studios, including the introduction of technicolour in 1932. That same year Walt Disney was awarded a special Oscar for the creation of Mickey Mouse.

Mickey's friends play an important role in the success of his cartoons, notably his devoted girlfriend Minnie whom he rescues from a variety of dangerous situations. Pluto, his playful pet dog, makes his appearance in 1930 and his dumb antics become the focus of attention in many of the shorts. Goofy is also a dog, beginning his career as Dippy Dawg in 1932, but he wears clothes and

walks on two legs so has a more human personality. He is described by his animator as an everlasting optimist, a half-wit and a good natured hick. He is always doing things wrong and ends up with a foolish apologetic laugh. He is a perfect foil for Mickey's other great friend, the hot-headed Donald Duck, who made his debut in 1934. If anyone crossed this cocky, boastful character he got mad and blew his top. Audiences loved his aggressive character, particularly as Mickey's own behaviour became more exemplary in response to his status as a major screen idol.

During the 1930s Disney became convinced that the future of animation lay in feature films as seven minute shorts were not cost effective and he began work on a major production of the Grimm Brothers' fairy tale, *Snow White and the Seven Dwarfs*. Hundreds of young animators were recruited to work around the clock on this daring new venture and his critics predicted bankruptcy. They also maintained that nobody would want to watch a cartoon for an hour or more and dubbed the enterprise 'Disney's Folly'. They could not have been more wrong. *Snow White* was a tremendous success when it was screened in 1938 and it went on to win an Academy Award for pioneering a 'great new entertainment field for the motion picture cartoon'. Several of the film's songs became hits and Snow White and the Dwarfs enjoyed the same merchandising success as Mickey and friends.

Disney immediately began work on a new project based on the story of Pinocchio by a 19th century Italian writer, Carlo Collodi. At first he struggled with the unsympathetic character of the

Walt Disney

Top left: Artwork for Snow White

Top right: Artwork for Happy

Centre right: Artwork for Doc

Below: Catalogue page of the Disney figures collection, 1954

puppet hero until he focused on the talking cricket as Pinocchio's conscience. In the original book, Pinocchio squashed the moralising insect with a mallet and his ghost guided the errant puppet but Disney kept Jiminy Cricket very much alive and gave him a lively personality, with plenty of funny quips to entertain and educate. Launched in 1940, *Pinocchio* was another great triumph.

When the Second World War began, the Disney animators were working on several major projects, including *Fantasia, Dumbo* and *Bambi,* the last feature-length production for a number of years. *Bambi,* which was released in 1942, was based on Felix Salten's book about a baby deer growing up in the forest and it was Disney's most lyrical and naturalistic film to date. Thumper, the mischievous rabbit who befriends Bambi, provides the comic relief for this essentially serious story and for many he is the star of the show.

Disney revived his feature film production in the 1950s beginning with the traditional fairy tale *Cinderella* (1950) which was one of his biggest box-office hits; *Alice in Wonderland* (1951), a less appealing interpretation of Lewis Carroll's classic and

WALT DISNEY FIGURES
COPYRIGHT

THUMPER 1291–3½"

PINOCCHIO 1282–4"

GOOFY 1281–4½"

TINKERBELL 1312–5"

PETER PAN 1307–5"

JIMINY CRICKET 1279–4"

NANA 1301–3½"

SMEE 1302–4½"

MICKEY MOUSE 1278–3½"

PLUTO 1280–3½"

DONALD DUCK 1283–4"

MINNIE MOUSE 1289–4"

Peter Pan (1953) a successful re-telling of James Barrie's fantasy about a little boy who never grew up. *Peter Pan* is full of wonderful characters, including the villainous Captain Hook, the bumbling Mr Smee, Nana the nursemaid dog and the curvaceous

fairy Tinker Bell, who steals many of the scenes although she never says a word. Tinker Bell went on to shower pixie dust in the Disneyland theme park and TV shows which preoccupied Walt Disney in the mid 1950s.

It was no doubt all the publicity surrounding the multi-media Disney Empire in the early 1950s which prompted the John Beswick studio to obtain a licence for reproducing some of the most famous cartoon stars in ceramic. A set of children's nursery ware was launched in 1954 featuring scenes of Goofy, Pluto, Mickey and Donald cycling on a tandem, and Bambi meeting Thumper. At the same time Jan Granoska, a young modeller from Eastern Europe who worked briefly in the Beswick studio, produced a series of figures portraying Mickey and Friends plus some of the stars from the feature films, including *Pinocchio* and *Jiminy Cricket, Thumper, Peter Pan, Mr Smee, Tinker Bell* and *Nana*. Like the cartoons, these were all very popular and remained in the range until 1965.

The task of capturing all the eccentricities of the Seven Dwarfs from the Disney classic was given to the chief modeller Arthur Gredington, who had immortalised David Hand's cartoon characters a few years earlier. Whilst his Dwarf figures are superb, he obviously struggled with his interpretation of Snow White as two versions exist with quite different hairstyles. To mark the 60th anniversary of Disney's first classic, three modellers from the Beswick studio collaborated on a limited edition collection of Snow White and the Seven Dwarfs and this was issued with a Royal Doulton backstamp in 1997. Snow White was also included in the Walt Disney *Princess* collection, launched in 1995. On this occasion, the lovely heroine was modelled by the talented Pauline Parsons and she is much larger than the other versions, standing eight inches tall. The limited edition *Princess* collection also includes *Cinderella, Aurora* from *Sleeping Beauty* (1959), *Jasmine* from *Aladdin* (1993), *Belle* from *Beauty and the Beast* (1991) and *Ariel* from *The Little Mermaid* (1989).

As can be seen from the last three films, the Disney studios are continuing to make box office history with their cartoon features, long after Walt's death in 1966.

Left: Advertisement for Disney nursery ware, 1954

Walt Disney

Snow White 1332 with two hairstyles left 1955-67 right 1954-55

They have also had many successes with their live action films, notably the 1996 remake of their animated classic *One Hundred and One Dalmatians* (1961). Starring Glenn Close as the villainous Cruella de Vil, this new interpretation gave a different twist to Dodie Smith's thrilling children's novel.

Royal Doulton also added a new dimension to the tale with their 1997 collection featuring the leading canine characters. Pongo and Perdita are the proud parents of fifteen Dalmatian puppies who get up to all sorts of mischief. In the limited edition group, Rolly is having his ear pulled by Freckles and another model shows him up to his neck in mud, obscuring some of his beautiful spotted coat. Because of their distinctive markings, the puppies are stolen by Cruella de Vil who wants to make them into a new fur coat. She holds them captive at her sinister mansion, Hell Hall, along with 84 other Dalmatian victims, but she is eventually out-witted by Pongo, Perdita and their animal friends. The outlandish Cruella, with her black and white hair and lavish furs, is undoubtedly the star of the show.

The Disney studios are not just dazzling cinema audiences, home viewers are entertained with video releases of their classic features and their own TV channel screened on both sides of the Atlantic. Disneyland theme parks have been established in Europe and Japan and their character merchandise continues to boom – each new movie will earn around $1 billion in licences. It's hard to believe this most magic of kingdoms was started by a mouse!

Mickey Mouse and Friends nursery ware produced by Paragon, c1930

Left: Minnie Mouse 1289, 1954-65

Right: Donald Duck 1283, 1954-65

Above: Mickey Mouse 1278, 1954-65

Left: Pluto 1280, 1954-65

Right: Goofy 1281, 1954-65

40

Walt Disney

Above: Pinocchio 1282, 1954-65

Left: Jiminy Cricket 1279, 1954-65

Above: Thumper 1291, 1954-65

Above: Artwork for Peter Pan cartoon, 1953

Left: Peter Pan 1307, 1954-65

Tinker Bell 1312, 1954-65

Above: Nana 1301, 1954-65

Right: Smee 1302, 1954-65

Walt Disney

OPPOSITE PAGE

Top left: Bashful 1327, 1955-67

Top right: Grumpy 1330, 1955-67

Centre: Snow White 1332, 1955-67

Bottom left: Doc 1329, 1955-67

Bottom centre: Sleepy 1331, 1955-67

Bottom right: Happy 1326, 1955-67

Top centre: Sneezy 1328, 1955-67

Top right: Dopey 1325, 1955-67

SNOW WHITE AND THE SEVEN DWARFS *(Second Series)*

Left to right: Doc SW2, Happy SW4, Sleepy SW7, Snow White SW1, Sneezy SW6, Dopey SW5, Grumpy SW3 and Bashful SW8, 1997-C

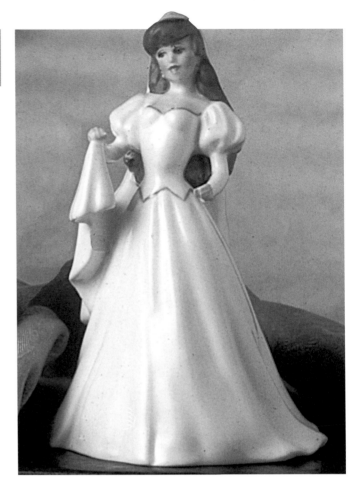

Top left: Snow White HN3678, 1995

Top right: Ariel HN3831, 1996

Bottom left: Cinderella HN3677, 1995

Bottom right: Jasmine HN3832, 1996

OPPOSITE PAGE

Top left: Belle HN3830, 1996

Bottom left: Aurora HN3833, 1996

Top right: Cruella de Vil HN3839, 1998

Bottom right: Maleficent HN3840, 1998

Walt Disney

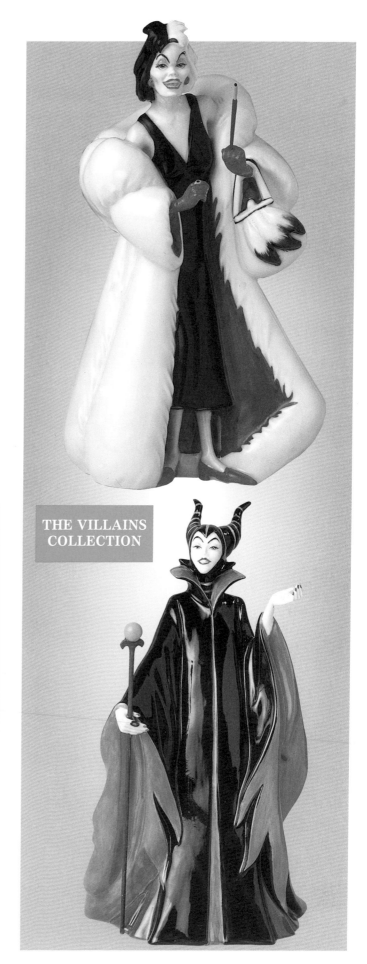

THE VILLAINS
COLLECTION

101 DALMATIANS COLLECTION

Left: Pongo DM6, 1997-C

Right: Perdita DM7, 1997-C

Below: Cruella de Vil DM1, 1997-C

Rolly DM4, 1997-C

Above: Lucky DM8, 1997–C

Right: Penny and Freckles DM3, 1997-C

46

Walt Disney

*Penny DM2,
1997-C*

*Patch, Rolly
and Freckles
DM5, 1997*

PATCH ROLLY
AND FRECKLES

WALT DISNEY

Mickey and Friends

John Beswick backstamp

1278   **Mickey Mouse**
Modelled by Jan Granoska
Height: 4 inches 10 cm
Introduced: 1954   Withdrawn: 1965

1280   **Pluto**
Modelled by Jan Granoska
Height: 3½ inches 8.5 cm
Introduced: 1954   Withdrawn: 1965

1281   **Goofy**
Modelled by Jan Granoska
Height: 4¼ inches 11.5 cm
Introduced: 1954   Withdrawn: 1965

1283   **Donald Duck**
Modelled by Jan Granoska
Height: 4 inches 10 cm
Introduced: 1954   Withdrawn: 1965

1289   **Minnie Mouse**
Modelled by Jan Granoska
Height: 4 inches 10 cm
Introduced: 1954   Withdrawn: 1965

Pinocchio

John Beswick backstamp

1279   **Jiminy Cricket**
Modelled by Jan Granoska
Height: 4 inches 10 cm
Introduced: 1954   Withdrawn: 1965

1282   **Pinocchio**
Modelled by Jan Granoska
Height: 4 inches 10 cm
Introduced: 1954   Withdrawn: 1965

Bambi

John Beswick backstamp

1291   **Thumper**
Modelled by Jan Granoska
Height: 3¾ inches 9.5 cm
Introduced: 1954   Withdrawn: 1965

Peter Pan

John Beswick backstamp

1301   **Nana**
Modelled by Jan Granoska
Height: 3¼ inches 8 cm
Introduced: 1954   Withdrawn: 1965

1302   **Smee**
Modelled by Jan Granoska
Height: 4¼ inches 10 cm
Introduced: 1954   Withdrawn: 1965

1307   **Peter Pan**
Modelled by Jan Granoska
Height: 5 inches 12.5 cm
Introduced: 1954   Withdrawn: 1965

1312   **Tinker Bell**
Modelled by Jan Granoska
Height: 5 inches 12.5 cm
Introduced: 1954   Withdrawn: 1965

Snow White

First Series

John Beswick backstamp

1325   **Dopey**
Modelled by Arthur Gredington
Height: 3½ inches 8.5 cm
Introduced: 1955   Withdrawn: 1967

1326   **Happy**
Modelled by Arthur Gredington
Height: 3½ inches 8.5 cm
Introduced: 1955   Withdrawn: 1967

1327   **Bashful**
Modelled by Arthur Gredington
Height: 3½ inches 8.5 cm
Introduced: 1955   Withdrawn: 1967

1328   **Sneezy**
Modelled by Arthur Gredington
Height: 3½ inches 8.5 cm
Introduced: 1955   Withdrawn: 1967

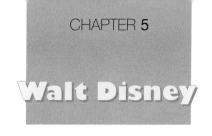

Walt Disney

1329   **Doc**
Modelled by Arthur Gredington
Height: 3½ inches 8.5 cm
Introduced: 1955   Withdrawn: 1967

1330   **Grumpy**
Modelled by Arthur Gredington
Height: 3½ inches 8.5 cm
Introduced: 1955   Withdrawn: 1967

1331   **Sleepy**
Modelled by Arthur Gredington
Height: 3½ inches 8.5 cm
Introduced: 1955   Withdrawn: 1967

1332   **Snow White**
Modelled by Arthur Gredington
Height: 5 inches 12.5 cm
Introduced: 1955   Withdrawn: 1967

Second Series

Royal Doulton backstamp. A special
commemorative mark was used in 1997 only

SW1   **Snow White**
Modelled by Amanda Hughes-Lubeck
Height: 5¾ inches 14.5 cm
Introduced in 1997 in a limited
edition of 2,000 and issued in 1998 in
an unlimited edition with a different
backstamp

SW2   **Doc**
Modelled by Amanda Hughes-Lubeck
Height: 3¼ inches 8 cm
Introduced in 1997 in a limited
edition of 2,000 and issued in 1998 in
an unlimited edition with a different
backstamp

SW3   **Grumpy**
Modelled by Shane Ridge
Height: 3½ inches 8.5 cm
Introduced in 1997 in a limited
edition of 2,000 and issued in 1998 in
an unlimited edition with a different
backstamp

SW4   **Happy**
Modelled by Amanda Hughes-Lubeck
Height: 3¾ inches 9.5 cm
Introduced in 1997 in a limited
edition of 2,000 and issued in 1998 in
an unlimited edition with a different
backstamp

SW5   **Dopey**
Modelled by Shane Ridge
Height: 3½ inches 8.5 cm
Introduced in 1997 in a limited
edition of 2,000 and issued in 1998 in
an unlimited edition with a different
backstamp

SW6   **Sneezy**
Modelled by Warren Platt
Height: 3½ inches 8.5 cm
Introduced in 1997 in a limited
edition of 2,000 and issued in 1998 in
an unlimited edition with a different
backstamp

SW7   **Sleepy**
Modelled by Warren Platt
Height: 3½ inches 8.5 cm
Introduced in 1997 in a limited
edition of 2,000 and issued in 1998 in
an unlimited edition with a different
backstamp

SW8   **Bashful**
Modelled by Amanda Hughes-Lubeck
Height: 3½ inches 8.5 cm
Introduced in 1997 in a limited
edition of 2,000 and issued in 1998 in
an unlimited edition with a different
backstamp

Princess Collection

Royal Doulton backstamp

HN3677 Cinderella
from *Cinderella*
Modelled by Pauline Parsons
Height: 8 inches 20.5 cm
Introduced: 1995
Commissioned by Disney
in a limited edition of 2,000

HN3678 Snow White
from *Snow White*
Modelled by Pauline Parsons
Height: 8 inches 20.5 cm
Introduced: 1995
Commissioned by Disney
in a limited edition of 2,000

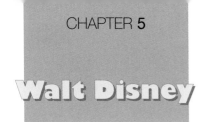

Walt Disney

HN3830 Belle

from *Beauty and the Beast*
Modelled by Pauline Parsons
Height: 8 inches 20.5 cm
Introduced: 1996
Commissioned by Disney
in a limited edition of 2,000

HN3831 Ariel

from *The Little Mermaid*
Modelled by Pauline Parsons
Height: 8 inches 20.5 cm
Introduced: 1996
Commissioned by Disney
in a limited edition of 2,000

HN3832 Jasmine

from *Aladdin*
Modelled by Pauline Parsons
Height: 8 inches 20.5 cm
Introduced: 1996
Commissioned by Disney
in a limited edition of 2,000

HN3833 Aurora

from *Sleeping Beauty*
Modelled by Pauline Parsons
Height: 8 inches 20.5 cm
Introduced: 1996
Commissioned by Disney
in a limited edition of 2,000

Villains Collection

Royal Doulton backstamp

HN3839 Cruella de Vil

from *101 Dalmatians*
Modelled by Pauline Parsons
Height: 8 inches 20.5 cm
Introduced: 1998
Commissioned by Disney
in a limited edition of 2,000

HN3840 Maleficent

from *Sleeping Beauty*
Modelled by Pauline Parsons
Height: 8 inches 20.5 cm
Introduced: 1998
Commissioned by Disney
in a limited edition of 2,000

101 Dalmatians

Royal Doulton backstamp

DM1 **Cruella de Vil**
Modelled by Martyn Alcock
Height: 6¼ inches 16 cm
Introduced: 1997 Still in production

DM2 **Penny**
Modelled by Shane Ridge
Height: 2¾ inches 7 cm
Introduced: 1997 Still in production

DM3 **Penny and Freckles**
Modelled by Shane Ridge
Height: 2¼ inches 5.5 cm
Introduced: 1997 Still in production

DM4 **Rolly**
Modelled by Shane Ridge
Height: 2¾ inches 7 cm
Introduced: 1997 Still in production

DM5 **Patch, Rolly and Freckles**
Modelled by Shane Ridge
Height: 3¾ inches 9.5 cm
Introduced in 1997 in a limited
edition of 3,500

DM6 **Pongo**
Modelled by Shane Ridge
Height: 4½ inches 11.5 cm
Introduced: 1997 Still in production

DM7 **Perdita**
Modelled by Martyn Alcock
Height: 2½ inches 6.5 cm
Introduced: 1997 Still in production

DM8 **Lucky**
Modelled by Martyn Alcock
Height: 2¾ inches 7 cm
Introduced: 1997 Still in production

WALT DISNEY NURSERY WARE

John Beswick backstamp

Produced from 1953 to 1971

Scenes
Micky Mouse and
Donald Duck cycling
Pluto
Goofy
Bambi and Thumper
Figaro
Piper Pig
Bluebird

Shapes
Plate 6 inch, baby plate, cereal bowl, mug, cup
and saucer and toy tea set

Winnie the Pooh

FOR 'a bear of little brain', Winnie the Pooh has been remarkably successful in the publishing, film and merchandising worlds. A A Milne first documented the teddy bear's adventures in 1926 and 150,000 copies of *Winnie the Pooh* were sold within a year. A contemporary critic described it as 'a book full of delight for all children under seventy' and it is still avidly read by fans of all ages and nationalities today. It has been published in 32 languages and the stories were even translated into Latin, becoming the first foreign language book ever to be a best seller on the *New York Times* list.

A second book, *The House at Pooh Corner,* was published in 1928 and many spin-offs followed, including cards, calendars, games and toys. By the early 1930s Winnie the Pooh was a thriving industry providing financial security for A A Milne who had sole reproduction rights for the text and the illustrations by E H Shepard. When Walt Disney filmed the books in the 1960s, Winnie the Pooh proved to be one of the most successful merchandising characters since Mickey Mouse. No less than 168 diverse items were tied in with the release of *Winnie the Pooh and the Honey Tree* in 1966 and more followed with the sequel cartoons. The John Beswick studio secured the rights to produce figures of all the main characters and the *Winnie the Pooh* collection was launched in 1968.

The story of Winnie the Pooh's transformation from nursery companion to international megastar is a fascinating one. He was the favourite toy of A A Milne's son, Christopher Robin,

Pooh and Piglet drawing

Above: Eeyore Loses a Tail WP15, 1997

and was named after a famous black bear at London zoo called Winnie and a swan encountered on a holiday in Arundel known to young Christopher as Pooh. Christopher Robin was already a public figure in the mid 1920s as the inspiration behind the poems *When We Were Young* and it was the success of this first children's book which encouraged Milne to dream up stories about his son's toys.

A major influence was Kenneth Grahame's *The Wind in the Willows* which Milne had adapted for the stage in 1921 as *Toad of Toad Hall*. It was undoubtedly his favourite book and he was always recommending it to his friends. One of the first questions he asked his future illustrator Ernest Shepard was whether he had read the book. Shepard's talents were not immediately recognised by Milne but his spontaneous drawings for *When We Were Young* altered his opinion. As one critic put it, Shepard's illustrations belong to the verses 'as intimately as the echo to the voice'. They continued to work together bringing Christopher Robin's toys to life in 'the enchanted place on top of the forest'. This was Ashdown Forest where the Milne family spent their weekends and all the stories are set firmly in real places which Shepard visited and drew. Cotchford Bridge, where Christopher Robin and Winnie the Pooh played pooh sticks, can still be seen today.

52

Winnie the Pooh

The activities shared by Christopher Robin and Winnie the Pooh are those which appeal to children everywhere, expeditions, tree houses, feasts, birthdays, songs and jokes. In the stories, Christopher Robin keeps the peace between his motley collection of toys, some of which were taken from real life and some imagined. For Christmas 1921 he received Eeyore, the donkey with the drooping neck which gave him a somewhat gloomy disposition. Piglet was a present from a neighbour but the original was chewed by a dog and replaced by another in a smaller size. Kanga and Roo were specially purchased from Harrods to add a new dimension to the stories and Owl and Rabbit were invented. The original toys are now in the New York Public Library, having travelled extensively in the US for promotional purposes during Milne's lifetime.

Tigger was originally an incidental character in the Milne stories but he became a star to rival Winnie the Pooh in the Disney interpretations. His extrovert personality dominated the later films such as *Winnie the Pooh and the Blustery Day* (1968) and *Winnie the Pooh and Tigger Too* (1974). Although the Disney films took their style from the Shepard illustrations, new characters were incorporated to temper the Britishness of the subject, notably a gopher with an American grass roots image. Shepard and his fans were critical of the results but the viewers' increased awareness of all the Winnie the Pooh characters encouraged sales of the original books. Collectors are also finding it increasingly expensive to acquire the original Beswick *Winnie the Pooh* figures which were produced until 1990. The good news is that a collection

Below left: Winnie the Pooh Christening gifts, 1995-C

Below right: Winnie the Pooh wall plates, 1995-C

of Royal Doulton *Winnie the Pooh* figures was introduced in 1996 to tie in with the gift ware collection. In the launch year, the figures all featured a special back-stamp to commemorate the 70th anniversary of the first Pooh book.

From time to time collectors have come across Winnie the Pooh designs on Lambeth ware, Doulton's robust everyday range. These were part of a breakfast set from the early 1980s which did not go into full production although examples were sold in some shops at the time. Winnie the Pooh fans might also like to look out for the original nursery set of twenty four pieces, inspired by scenes from all of Milne's books, which was made by the Ashstead Potteries in Surrey in 1928. The first hand painted sets were presented to Princess Elizabeth and Christopher Robin but later sets were transfer printed. Examples are now very hard to find.

A compromise was reached in Royal Doulton's series of nursery ware and gift ware which was launched in the UK in 1995. The designs combine Shepard's original line illustrations with the lively colour from the Disney films, notably Winnie the Pooh's vivid red waistcoat. A different collection, called *Classic Pooh*, was produced for the USA in 1997. In these designs, Pooh does not wear a waistcoat and the scenes are decorated in more pastel colours.

The timeless appeal of the characters from *Winnie the Pooh* was anticipated by A A Milne in his closing words: 'Wherever they go and whatever happens to them on the way, in that enchanted place on the top of the forest a little boy and his bear will always be playing'.

"Oh, Bear!" said Christopher Robin,
"How I do love you!"
"So do I," said Pooh.

Winnie the Pooh Lambethware
for market research only, 1980s

54

Winnie the Pooh

FIRST SERIES

Above: Owl 2216, 1969-89

Left: Rabbit 2215, 1969-89

Top right: Christopher Robin 2395, 1972-89

Below: Winnie the Pooh 2193, 1969-89

Piglet 2214, 1969-89

Kanga 2217, 1969-89

Eeyore 2196, 1969-89

Tigger 2394, 1972-89

*Left: Pooh Counting the
Honey Pots WP12, 1997-C*

*Centre: Eeyore's Tail
WP7, 1996-C*

*Right: Winnie the Pooh in
the Armchair WP4, 1996-C*

*Above left: Pooh's Blue Balloon
Money Ball WP16 1997-C*

*Above right: Piglet and
Balloon WP5, 1997-C*

*Left: Pooh Lights the
Candle WP11, 1997-C*

*Centre: Eeyore's
Birthday WP14,
1997-C*

*Right: Winnie the Pooh
and Honey Pot WP1,
1996-C*

Winnie the Pooh

Piglet Picking the Violets WP13, 1997-C

*Pooh and Piglet —
the Windy Day WP2,
1996-C*

*Above: Winnie the Pooh
and the Paw-marks WP3,
1996-97*

*Right: Christopher Robin
and Pooh WP10, 1996-97*

*Below: Christopher Robin
WP9, 1996-C*

*Kanga and Roo
WP8, 1996-C*

Tigger Signs the Risolution WP6, 1996-C

WINNIE THE POOH

First Series

John Beswick backstamp
Designed by Harry Sales

2193 Winnie the Pooh
Modelled by Albert Hallam
Height: 2½ inches 6.5 cm
Introduced: 1969   Withdrawn: 1989

2196 Eeyore
Modelled by Albert Hallam
Height: 2 inches 5.5 cm
Introduced: 1969   Withdrawn: 1989

2214 Piglet
Modelled by Albert Hallam
Height: 2¾ inches 7 cm
Introduced: 1969   Withdrawn: 1989

2215 Rabbit
Modelled by Albert Hallam
Height: 3 inches 7.5 cm
Introduced: 1969   Withdrawn: 1989

2216 Owl
Modelled by Albert Hallam
Height: 3 inches 7.5 cm
Introduced: 1969   Withdrawn: 1989

2217 Kanga
Modelled by Albert Hallam
Height: 3 inches 7.5 cm
Introduced: 1969   Withdrawn: 1989

2394 Tigger
Modelled by Graham Tongue
Height: 3 inches 7.5 cm
Introduced: 1972   Withdrawn: 1989

2395 Christopher Robin
Modelled by Graham Tongue
Height: 4¾ inches 12 cm
Introduced: 1972   Withdrawn: 1989

Second Series

Royal Doulton backstamp. A special
commemorative mark was used in 1996 only

**WP1 Winnie the Pooh and the
Honey Pot**
Modelled by Warren Platt
Height: 2½ inches 6.5 cm
Introduced: 1996   Still in production

WP2 Pooh and Piglet — The Windy Day
Modelled by Martyn Alcock
Height: 3½ inches 8.5 cm
Introduced: 1996   Still in production

**WP3 Winnie the Pooh and the
Paw Marks**
Modelled by Warren Platt
Height: 2¾ inches 7 cm
Introduced: 1996   Withdrawn: 1997

WP4 Winnie the Pooh in the Armchair
Modelled by Shane Ridge
Height: 3½ inches 8.5 cm
Introduced: 1996   Still in production

WP5 Piglet and Balloon
Modelled by Warren Platt
Height: 2¾ inches 7 cm
Introduced: 1996   Still in production

WP6 Tigger Signs the Risolution
Modelled by Martyn Alcock
Height: 1¾ inches 4.5 cm
Introduced: 1996   Still in production

WP7 Eeyore's Tail
Modelled by Shane Ridge
Height: 3½ inches 8.5 cm
Introduced: 1996   Still in production

WP8 Kanga and Roo
Modelled by Martyn Alcock
Height: 3¾ inches 9.5 cm
Introduced: 1996   Still in production

WP9 Christopher Robin
Modelled by Shane Ridge
Height: 5½ inches 13.5 cm
Introduced: 1996   Still in production

WP10 Christopher Robin and Pooh
Modelled by Shane Ridge
Height: 3½ inches 8.5 cm
Introduced: 1996   Withdrawn: 1997

WP11 Pooh Lights the Candle
Modelled by Graham Tongue
Height: 3¾ inches 9.5 cm
Introduced: 1997   Still in production

WP12 Pooh Counting the Honeypots
Modelled by Martyn Alcock
Height: 3¾ inches 9.5 cm
Introduced: 1997   Still in production

WP13 Piglet Picking the Violets
Modelled by Graham Tongue
Height: 2½ inches 6.5 cm
Introduced: 1997   Still in production

WP14 Eeyore's Birthday
Modelled by Martyn Alcock
Height: 2¾ inches 7 cm
Introduced: 1997   Still in production

WP15 Eeyore Loses a Tail
Modelled by Martyn Alcock
Height: 4 inches 10 cm
Introduced: 1997 in a limited edition
of 5,000

WP16 Pooh's Blue Balloon Money Ball
Modelled by Shane Ridge
Height: 4¼ inches 10.5 cm
Introduced: 1997   Still in production

WINNIE THE POOH NURSERY AND GIFT WARE

UK Collection — all current

Royal Doulton backstamp
Designed by Justin Clark after illustrations by
E H Shepard and Disney

Wall plates
The Woozle 1995
Poohsticks 1995
The Honey Tree 1995
The Rescue 1995
Merry Christmas 1996

Mugs
Eeyore's House 1995
Pooh's Basket 1995
Playing Poohsticks 1995
Pooh in the River 1995
Getting Thin 1995
We Might Go in Your Umbrella 1997
Dangerous Place 1997
Eeyore Has Lost a Tail 1997
To Catch a Heffalump 1997

Nursery ware
Plate 8 inches — Pooh and Friends Eating 1995
Baby plate — Pooh and Piglet in the Snow 1995
Cereal bowl — Pooh and Piglet in the Snow 1995
Hug-a-Mug 1 handle — Pooh Looking in the
    Cupboard 1995
Hug-a-Mug 2 handles — Pooh Pinning on
    Eeyore's Tail 1995

Tea cups and saucers
Poohsticks 1996
The Woozle 1996
Honey Tree 1996
The Rescue 1996
Merry Christmas 1996

Gift ware
Wall clock 'Nearly eleven o'clock' 1995
Mantel clock 1997
Photograph frame — Pooh with Balloon 1995
Money ball — Pooh Looking in the Cupboard 1995

Gift Sets
Christening set — Pooh and Friends with
    Baby 1995
Comprising 8 inch plate, money ball and
    hug-a-mug with 1 handle
These items are also sold individually

Children's set — stock designs 1995
Comprising 8 inch plate, cereal bowl and
    hug-a-mug with 1 handle
Infant's set — stock designs 1995
Comprising cereal bowl and hug-a-mug with 1
    handle
Baby's set — stock designs 1995
Comprising baby plate and hug-a-mug with 1
    handle
Miniature tea set — 1996
Commissioned by Gabrielle House to
    accompany a mohair Pooh Bear

US Collection — Classic Pooh — all current

Mugs
Pooh with Piglet in Armchair 1997
Christopher Robin Reading to Pooh 1997

Gift Ware
Clock — Christopher Robin and Pooh catching
    Tigger 1997
Savings Book — Christopher Robin, Pooh and
    Piglet Playing Poohsticks 1997
Photograph Frame 1997

Baby's Set — Pooh with Tigger at the Table
    and Pooh with Piglet in the Armchair 1997
Comprising baby plate and hug-a-mug with 2
    handles

Children's Set — Christopher Robin with
    Pooh and Piglet, Pooh at the Cupboard and
    Christopher Robin Reading to Pooh 1997
Comprising 8 inch plate, cereal bowl and hug-a-
    mug with 1 handle

Joan Walsh Anglund

OPPOSITE PAGE

*Anglund Boy 2272,
1970-71*

Below: Pages from
Look out of the Window
by Joan Walsh Anglund

WHEN Joan Walsh Anglund wrote and illustrated her first book *A Friend is Someone Who Likes You* in 1958, it was chosen by the *New York Times* as one of the ten best children's books that year. It became an immediate best seller and over 3 million copies have been sold around the world.

Joan Walsh Anglund produced more than 25 picture books for children, including *Love is a Special Way of Feeling, A is for Always* and *What Color is Love,* and these also became worldwide favourites. The secret of her success was presenting a single idea in a simple way without confusion, making her books ideal for very young children. Her method of drawing little girls and boys, with just dots for eyes and no other features, was almost child-like in its simplicity. However, her sophisticated graphic style can be seen in all the detailed costumes and backgrounds as well as in the faces of the adults represented.

As the child of artists, Mrs Anglund found that drawing and writing came naturally to her. From a young age, she spent many hours reading and designing illustrations for her favourite books. A career in art was the obvious choice and she studied drawing and painting at the Art Institute of Chicago as well as the American Academy of Art. In addition to producing her own books, she worked for National Magazines and her distinctive drawing style became very well known during the 1960s.

Illustration from Look Out of the Window

Rag dolls, based on her designs, were popular with young children and led to other licensed products, such as the Beswick figures.

Harry Sales, the Design Manager of the Beswick factory, was sent a selection of her books when they were published in the UK and he chose three typical subjects for the Beswick figures which were modelled by Albert Hallam. Unfortunately, the Anglund figures only stayed in production for a couple of years and so they are very hard to find today.

Box for Flower Girl figure

Joan Walsh Anglund

*Anglund Flower Girl
2317, 1971*

Anglund Boy 2272, 1970-71

*Anglund Girl with Doll
2293, 1970-71*

JOAN WALSH ANGLUND

John Beswick backstamp

Designed by Harry Sales

2272   Anglund Boy
Modelled by Albert Hallam
Height: 4½ inches 12 cm
Introduced: 1970   Withdrawn: 1971

2293   Anglund Girl with Doll
Modelled by Albert Hallam
Height: 4½ inches 12 cm
Introduced: 1970   Withdrawn: 1971

2317   Anglund Flower Girl
Modelled by Albert Hallam
Height: 4¾ inches 12 cm
Introduced: 1971   Withdrawn: 1971

Kitty MacBride

Kitty MacBride

AMUSING CHARACTER mice were amongst the first figures to be produced by the Doulton factory. At the studios in Lambeth, George Tinworth modelled groups of mice reflecting his homespun philosophies during the 1880s. Nearly a century later, the Beswick factory promoted Kitty MacBride's mice groups as the perfect vehicles to express the vanities, joys and foibles of human beings.

Before she began producing her 'Happy Mice', Kitty MacBride had enjoyed a successful career as a journalist, fiction writer and illustrator. Her interest in pottery began in the early 1960s when she kept some field mice in a glass fronted cage so that she could observe them more closely. She spent many hours sketching their antics and then decided to model them in clay. Before long her mice figures were wearing clothes and involved in human pursuits, such as dancing or reading. Her subjects were chosen to cheer people up as she believed there are too many depressing things in the world. Invariably she raised a smile with the humorous expressions of the mice and her whimsical inscriptions and titles. In *A Good Read* the little mouse is engrossed in 'Batmouse Flies Again' whilst in *Strained Relations* the indignant female mouse challenges 'Are you a mouse or a man'.

Mrs MacBride's charmingly naive style of modelling is in the tradition of the old Staffordshire figures and connoisseurs of 18th and 19th century country pottery have particularly valued her work, with several examples being acquired by museums in America. Originally she sold all her 'Happy Mice' through a London dealer and attracted many famous collectors from the arts world. Special commissions included a model for former Prime Minister Edward Heath and a series for the late Cardinal Heenan which illustrated his career from parish priest to cardinal.

Such was the demand for Mrs MacBride's mice models that she eventually approached the Beswick factory to have them reproduced in greater numbers. Modellers Graham Tongue and David Lyttleton skilfully interpreted her original models for factory production and the Kitty MacBride collection was

OPPOSITE PAGE

All I Do Is Think Of You
2589, 1977-83

launched in 1976. Several of the Beswick subjects focus on romance and relationships and titles such as *All I Do is Think of You, Guilty Sweethearts* and *The Ring* were produced as gifts for young couples. Others, such as *Lazybones* and *The Snack*, gently poked fun at human weaknesses. The eleven Kitty MacBride figures were discontinued in 1983 and all are collectable today although *A Good Read* and *All I Do is Think of You* are the most sought after and consequently the most expensive.

Above: Lazybones 2530, 1976-82

Left: The Ring 2565, 1976-83

Right: A Family Mouse 2526, 1976-82

Kitty MacBride

*Centre: All I Do Is
Think Of You
2589, 1977-83*

*Above: A Good Read
2529, 1976-82*

*A Snack 2531,
1976-82*

*Strained
Relations 2532,
1976-82*

Right: Double Act 2527, 1976-82

Below: The Racegoer 2528, 1976-82

Just Good Friends 2533, 1976-82

Left: Guilty Sweethearts 2566, 1976-83

KITTY MACBRIDE

John Beswick backstamp

2526   **A Family Mouse**
Modelled by Graham Tongue
Height: 3½ inches 8.5 cm
Introduced: 1976   Withdrawn: 1982

2527   **A Double Act**
Modelled by Graham Tongue
Height: 3½ inches 8.5 cm
Introduced: 1976   Withdrawn: 1982

2528   **The Racegoer**
Modelled by David Lyttleton
Height: 3½ inches 8.5 cm
Introduced: 1976   Withdrawn: 1982

2529   **A Good Read**
Modelled by David Lyttleton
Height: 3½ inches 8.5 cm
Introduced: 1976   Withdrawn: 1982

2530   **Lazybones**
Modelled by David Lyttleton
Height: 1½ inches 4 cm
Introduced: 1976   Withdrawn: 1982

2531   **A Snack**
Modelled by David Lyttleton
Height: 3¼ inches 8 cm
Introduced: 1976   Withdrawn: 1982

2532   **Strained Relations**
Modelled by David Lyttleton
Height: 3 inches 7.5 cm
Introduced: 1976   Withdrawn: 1982

2533   **Just Good Friends**
Modelled by David Lyttleton
Height: 3 inches 7.5 cm
Introduced: 1976   Withdrawn: 1982

2565   **The Ring**
Modelled by David Lyttleton
Height: 3¼ inches 8 cm
Introduced: 1976   Withdrawn: 1983

2566   **Guilty Sweethearts**
Modelled by David Lyttleton
Height: 2¼ inches 5.5 cm
Introduced: 1976   Withdrawn: 1983

2589   **All I Do is Think of You**
Modelled by David Lyttleton
Height: 2½ inches 6.5 cm
Introduced: 1977   Withdrawn: 1983

Kitty MacBride ©
"A Double Act"
2527
BESWICK
ENGLAND

CHAPTER
9

Alice in Wonderland

Alice in Wonderland

OPPOSITE PAGE
*The Mad Hatter 2479,
1975-81*

*Right and below:
Illustrations from* Alice's
Adventures in Wonderland
by John Tenniel

'DOWN, DOWN, DOWN. Would the fall never come to an end' wailed Alice as she plunged down the rabbit hole into Wonderland. There, everything grows 'curiouser and curiouser' as she meets the bizarre residents of this extraordinary fantasy world created by Charles Dodgson, an Oxford don writing under the pen name of Lewis Carroll. Never before had such a marvellous story been created for children without any moral purpose. With its brilliant use of nonsense, *Alice's Adventures in Wonderland* marked a turning point in children's literature when it was first published in 1865 and it still continues to enthral young readers today.

During the last century, Lewis Carroll's masterpiece has been translated into countless languages and has inspired an operetta, a stage play and several films, including a Disney cartoon. Artists in other media have been equally fascinated with Carroll's weird creations, offering diverse interpretations of *Alice's Adventures in Wonderland* and its sequel *Through the Looking Glass,* but perhaps the best known images are those of the original illustrator Sir John Tenniel. This superb draughtsman made his reputation as an illustrator of *Aesop's Fables* in 1848 and was a regular contributor to *Punch* magazine, producing over 2,000 drawings in his 50 year association with the periodical.

Royal Doulton artists first sought inspiration from the pages of *Alice's Adventures in Wonderland* in 1906 just as the copyright was due to expire. Lots of the favourite characters, loosely derived from Tenniel's illustrations, are depicted on a large set of children's nursery ware, which remained in production until 1932. Pieces are hard to find today, no doubt because the fine bone china body was not best suited to the rough and tumble of nursery life. In 1940, a freelance Beswick artist, Miss Joachim, produced four designs depicting characters from the classic tale modelled in relief but these are only known from pattern book illustrations and there is some doubt if they actually went into production.

Some years later, in 1960, Peggy Davies modelled *Alice* (HN2158), a delightful figure of a little girl reading the classic tale. The pages of her tiny book depict a drawing and verses from the *Walrus and the Carpenter*, which can be read with the aid of a magnifying glass. The original Alice, who inspired the adventures, was the daughter of Reverend George Liddell, Dean of Christ Church in Oxford and Head of the College where Charles Dodgson taught mathematics. A rather reserved bachelor, Dodgson was happiest in the company of children, entertaining them with conjuring tricks and all manner of games and puzzles. He was also a very talented photographer, excelling in portraits of pretty girls and the enchanting Alice Liddell became one of his models as well as a dear friend.

The story of Alice's adventures underground began during a river picnic with the heroine, then ten years old, and two of her sisters. Becoming restless, Alice begged for a story 'with plenty of nonsense in it' and Dodgson obliged. Later he wrote down the tale, adding some of his own drawings, but it was not until two years later that he was persuaded to publish it adding new characters and commissioning professional illustrations for, as Alice remarked on page one, 'What is the use of a book without pictures'.

The Tenniel pictures certainly proved very useful for Royal Doulton modeller Max Henk who used them as the basis for three character jugs, which were introduced to mark the centenary of Alice's Adventures in 1965. The *Mad Hatter*, the *Ugly Duchess* and the *Walrus and the Carpenter* character jugs have proved to be very popular with collectors, as have the 1980s additions to the *Wonderland* range, the *Red Queen*, the *Cook and the Cheshire Cat* and the *March Hare*.

The Beswick Design Manager, Harry Sales, also consulted Tenniel's originals when he was asked to produce an *Alice* series of figures in 1973. He provided the Beswick

Design for the Cheshire Cat by Harry Sales

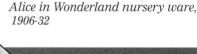

Left: Design for the Mock Turtle by Harry Sales

Alice in Wonderland nursery ware, 1906-32

Alice in Wonderland

modellers, Albert Hallam and Graham Tongue, with detailed drawings for the eleven subjects. Some modifications took place during the modelling process, most notably with the *Cheshire Cat* who loses his manic toothy grin in the finished piece and enjoys a more relaxed snooze. It would appear that the cat, who is prone to vanishing in the story, is equally elusive in the marketplace as it is now the most expensive piece in this very desirable collection which was withdrawn in 1981.

Other particular favourites include *Alice*, the *White Rabbit* who lures her into Wonderland and the *Mad Hatter*, who is depicted with a teacup in one hand and a piece of bread and butter in the other, just as he appears at the trial of the Knave of Hearts. The *King* and *Queen of Hearts*, who preside over this farcical court case, were also fashioned into Beswick figures. Less well known characters include the *Fish* and *Frog Footmen*, who brought the invitation to the crazy croquet match, and the *Gryphon* who danced the Lobster Quadrille and took Alice to meet the *Mock Turtle*, who sobbingly told her how he used to be a real turtle.

One of the last figures to join the collection in 1975 was the *Dodo*, which was inspired by the last remaining stuffed example

Right: Mad Hatter character jug D6598. modelled by Max Henk, 1965-83

Ugly Duchess character jug D6599, modelled by Max Henk, 1965-73

Right: March Hare character jug D6776, modelled by Bill Harper, 1989-91

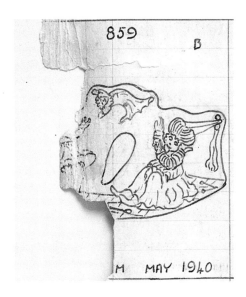

of this extinct bird in the Oxford University Museum. Alice and Charles Dodgson knew this exhibit well and it became the writer's nickname as he had a slight stutter and sometimes introduced himself as Do-Do Dodgson.

Although Alice's adventures in Wonderland turned out to be a curious dream, there are lots of tangible mementoes of her visit thanks to the Doulton and Beswick artists. Like Alice, keen collectors can now escape from dull reality with a nostalgic Wonderland display and, in the words of Lewis Carroll, remember their 'own child-life and happy summer days'.

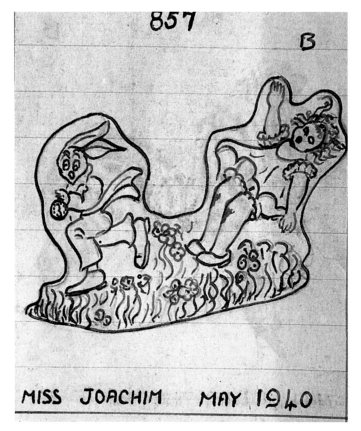

Above: Cheshire Cat 2480, 1975-81

Right: Alice 2476, 1975-81

Below Left: White Rabbit 2477, 1975-81

Below Centre: Mad Hatter 2479, 1975-81

Below Right: Gryphon 2485, 1975-81

Above: Frog Footman 2547, 1976-81

Top centre: King of Hearts 2489, 1975-81

Below: Mock Turtle 2478, 1975-81

Above: Fish Footman 2546, 1976-81

Below centre: Dodo 2545, 1976-81

Below : Queen of Hearts 2490, 1975-81

Alice in Wonderland

ALICE IN WONDERLAND

First Series

John Beswick backstamp

857 Alice and the White Rabbit
Modelled by Miss Joachim
Introduced: 1940   Withdrawn: 1940

858 The Dormouse and Alice Plaque
Modelled by Miss Joachim
Introduced: 1940   Withdrawn: 1940

859 The King and Alice Plaque
Modelled by Miss Joachim
Introduced: 1940   Withdrawn: 1940

860 Alice Playing Croquet
Modelled by Miss Joachim
Introduced: 1940   Withdrawn: 1940

ALICE IN WONDERLAND NURSERY WARE

Royal Doulton backstamp
Produced from 1906 to 1932 after illustrations
by John Tenniel

Scenes

Alice and the Duchess
Alice and the Dormouse
Alice and the Caterpillar
The King and the Hatter
The Mock Turtle
The Three Gardeners
Alice and the Queen
Alice and the Rabbit
The Dormouse
The Queen
The Two Footmen
The Blue Caterpillar
The King
The Mad Hatter (standing)
The Mad Hatter (seated)
Father William and the Youth
Father William (standing on his head)
The White Rabbit
The Duchess

Shapes

Plates, beaker, baby plate, cereal bowl, sugar
and cream, tea cup and saucer, miniatures

Pattern numbers

D2863, D5180, E4021, E4090, E5180, E5187

Second Series

John Beswick backstamp
Designed by Harry Sales

2476 Alice
Modelled by Albert Hallam and
Graham Tongue
Height: 4³/₄ inches 12 cm
Introduced: 1975   Withdrawn: 1981

2477 White Rabbit
Modelled by Graham Tongue
Height: 4³/₄ inches 12 cm
Introduced: 1975   Withdrawn: 1981

2478 Mock Turtle
Modelled by Graham Tongue
Height: 4¹/₄ inches 10.5 cm
Introduced: 1975   Withdrawn: 1981

2479 Mad Hatter
Modelled by Graham Tongue
Height: 4¹/₄ inches 10.5 cm
Introduced: 1975   Withdrawn: 1981

2480 Cheshire Cat
Modelled by Graham Tongue
Height: 1³/₄ inches 4.5 cm
Introduced: 1975   Withdrawn: 1981

2485 Gryphon
Modelled by Albert Hallam
Height: 3¹/₄ inches 8 cm
Introduced: 1975   Withdrawn: 1981

2489 King of Hearts
Modelled by Graham Tongue
Height: 3³/₄ inches 9.5 cm
Introduced: 1975   Withdrawn: 1981

2490 Queen of Hearts
Modelled by Graham Tongue
Height: 4 inches 10 cm
Introduced: 1975   Withdrawn: 1981

2545 Dodo
Modelled by David Lyttleton
Height: 4 inches 10 cm
Introduced: 1976   Withdrawn: 1981

2546 Fish Footman
Modelled by David Lyttleton
Height: 4³/₄ inches 12 cm
Introduced: 1976   Withdrawn: 1981

2547 Frog Footman
Modelled by David Lyttleton
Height: 4¹/₄ inches 10.5 cm
Introduced: 1976   Withdrawn: 1981

2295 Display stand
Height: 2¹/₂ inches 6.5 cm
Introduced: 1977   Withdrawn: 1997
This was also used for other series
and from 1989 to 1997 carried a
Royal Doulton backstamp.

The Lord of the Rings

'IN THE land of Mordor dwelt Sauron, dreaded Lord of the Rings, growing in evil power and threatening to cast his baleful shadow over all the free peoples of the kingdoms of Middle-Earth. But before he can subjugate them to his eternal dominion, he needs to find the one Ring of Power, lost long ago in a previous struggle.

Frodo, a young Hobbit from the half-forgotten Shire, has by fate come into possession of that very ring. To vanquish Sauron for ever, it must be destroyed. Yet the only place this can be accomplished is the fires of Mount Doom, at the very heart of Sauron's realm.

Battles rage and mighty armies clash, but Frodo must go on alone with his terrible burden, followed only by faithful Samwise and treacherous Gollum.'

J R R Tolkien's epic tale of Middle Earth, an imaginary world with its own mythology, has enthralled readers young and old since it was first published in 1954. Entitled *The Lord of the Rings,* it was written as a sequel to his successful children's book *The Hobbit* (1937) but over the years it became more serious and grew to such vast proportions that it was eventually published in three volumes.

By the mid 1960s, the trilogy had become an international best seller. A campus cult began in the USA where many young people identified acceptable heroes for their counter culture in Tolkien's mythology. Hobbitomania eventually led to an animated film version of *The Lord of the Rings* which was produced by Saul Zaentz of Berkeley, California in 1978.

Right: The Lord of the Rings fotonovel

OPPOSITE PAGE
Gandalf HN2911, 1980-84

Page from The Lord of the Rings
fotonovel

Tolkien drew upon his profound knowledge of Germanic, Celtic and Norse literature to invent his own coherent fantasy world. As a boy he had been much influenced by all the fairy literature fashionable in the Edwardian period and, during his English language studies at Oxford University, he began writing fairy poetry and prose. At the very young age of 33, he became Professor of Anglo-Saxon at Oxford and he shared his time between his teaching commitments, his writing and his children, who enjoyed his marvellously inventive bedtime stories, several of which were published.

Tolkien believed that fairy stories are not just for children but can appeal to the imagination of all readers if they are prepared to surrender themselves to the fantasy. The heroic romance which takes place in Middle Earth is compelling and convincing, with maps to follow and every detail of natural history and geology worked out. As the book casts its spell, it seems entirely feasible that the earth was once populated by elves, dwarves and small tubby Hobbits with large hairy feet.

In 1980, Royal Doulton made these extraordinary characters even more tangible when they launched a collection of small scale figures under license from Tolkien Enterprises. The Saul Zaentz

The Lord of the Rings

film provided references for some of the twelve characters in the set, whilst for others designer Harry Sales was inspired by images conjured up by Tolkien's detailed descriptions.

The collection was introduced over three years and the first four feature the leading personalities: *Bilbo* (HN2914) the Hobbit who originally found the Ring; *Frodo* (HN2912), his young cousin whose task it is to hide it forever; *Gandalf* (HN2911) the wise wizard who guides him and their loathsome foe *Gollum* (HN2913) who was utterly corrupted by the power of the Ring, his 'precious'. Many other colourful characters help them on their amazing adventure: *Samwise* (HN2925), Frodo's faithful servant; *Barliman Butterbur* (HN2923), a jovial innkeeper; the brave *Aragorn* (HN2916), first king of the reunited kingdom; the elves *Legolas* (HN2917) and *Galadriel* (HN2915), *Boromir* (HN2918) the man warrior, *Gimli* (HN2922) the dwarf, and the merry fellow *Tom Bombadil* (HN2924). A ceramic display stand, combining craggy rocks and gnarled roots in the spirit of Middle Earth, was designed to complement the figures in 1982.

The *Lord of the Rings* figures were all discontinued in January 1984 at the end of the four year license period and they are increasingly difficult to find today. However, the rarest are *Barliman Butterbur, Samwise,* and *Tom Bombadil* as they were produced for less than two years and they now change hands for at least ten times their issue price.

Design for The Lord of the Rings collection by Harry Sales

IMMERSE 'RING' IN WATER RESIN.

WATER EFFECT.

Above: Tom Bombadil HN2924, 1982-84

Centre left: Boromir HN2918, 1981-84

Centre right: Legolas HN2917, 1981-84

Bottom left: Barliman Butterbur HN2923, 1982-84

Bottom right: Gimli HN2922, 1981-84

The Lord of the Rings

Above: Galadriel HN2915, 1981-84

Top left: Aragorn HN2916, 1981-84

Top right: Gandalf HN2911, 1980-84

Centre left: Bilbo HN2914, 1980-84

Centre right: Gollum HN2913, 1980-84

The Lord of the Rings

Left: Samwise HN2925, 1982-84

Right: Frodo HN2912, 1980-84

THE LORD OF THE RINGS

Royal Doulton backstamp
Designed by Harry Sales

HN2911 Gandalf
Modelled by David Lyttleton
Height: 7 inches 17.5 cm
Introduced: 1980   Withdrawn: 1984

HN2912 Frodo
Modelled by David Lyttleton
Height: 4½ inches 11.5 cm
Introduced: 1980   Withdrawn: 1984

HN2913 Gollum
Modelled by David Lyttleton
Height: 3¼ inches 8 cm
Introduced: 1980   Withdrawn: 1984

HN2914 Bilbo
Modelled by David Lyttleton
Height: 4¼ inches 10.5 cm
Introduced: 1980   Withdrawn: 1984

HN2915 Galadriel
Modelled by David Lyttleton
Height: 5½ inches 13.5 cm
Introduced: 1981   Withdrawn: 1984

HN2916 Aragorn
Modelled by David Lyttleton
Height: 6 inches 15 cm
Introduced: 1981   Withdrawn: 1984

HN2917 Legolas
Modelled by David Lyttleton
Height: 6 inches 15 cm
Introduced: 1981   Withdrawn: 1984

HN2918 Boromir
Modelled by David Lyttleton
Height: 6¼ inches 16 cm
Introduced: 1981   Withdrawn: 1984

HN2922 Gimli
Modelled by David Lyttleton
Height: 5½ inches 13.5 cm
Introduced: 1981   Withdrawn: 1984

HN2923 Barliman Butterbur
Modelled by David Lyttleton
Height: 5¼ inches 13 cm
Introduced: 1982   Withdrawn: 1984

HN2924 Tom Bombadil
Modelled by David Lyttleton
Height: 5¾ inches 14.5 cm
Introduced: 1982   Withdrawn: 1984

HN2925 Samwise
Modelled by David Lyttleton
Height: 4½ inches 11.5 cm
Introduced: 1982   Withdrawn: 1984

Thelwell

*Design for Lady Jockeys
Rule OK resin figure by
Harry Sales
Not produced*

*Pony Express
2789G,
1983-89*

ANGELS ON HORSEBACK by Norman Thelwell was first published in 1957 and has never been out of print. It was followed by several more titles, featuring humorous drawings of shaggy ponies getting the better of their young owners, and these have inspired millions of aspiring young riders around the world.

Although Thelwell is a very versatile artist, it was the pony theme that assured his international reputation. He began his artistic career just after the war as Art Director of Army Publications in New Delhi and then went on to train at Liverpool School of Art before being offered a teaching post at Wolverhampton College. In 1952, he first submitted work to *Punch* magazine and, during an association that lasted 25 years, he produced more than 1,500 drawings including 60 front covers. His subjects explored the humour of the British countryside and rural pursuits and in 1953 he happened to submit a cartoon depicting a child with her pony at the blacksmith's shop. This prompted so much interest that he was encouraged to pursue the pony theme in *Punch* and his first book was a compilation of these published cartoons.

Thelwell gave up teaching in 1955 after being offered a job as a cartoonist with the *News Chronicle* and he also worked freelance as a book and magazine illustrator. His growing reputation for pony cartoons led to a commission to produce a humorous book of riding instructions for pony-mad kids and *A Leg at Each Corner* was full of hilarious drawings exploiting the precarious relationship between horse and rider. A strip cartoon followed in the *Sunday Express* and before long lots of children's ponies were being named Kipper after his cartoon horse or even Thelwell. Kipper was so called because he was half asleep when he was not giving his owner Penelope a hard time.

By 1975, Thelwell had sold over a million books in paperback, not to mention all the hardback sales, and a minor industry was developing in the merchandising of his characters and drawings.

thelwell

When Royal Doulton's Marketing Director was looking around for new characters for the 'World of Imagination' collection, the pony cartoons seemed an ideal choice. Design Manager Harry Sales worked very closely with Norman Thelwell in the interpretation of his cartoons for ceramic and he is the proud owner of several Thelwell 'doodles' which the cartoonist dashed off during his visits.

Box and figure for Studio Sculptures collection

Harry has certainly captured the essence of Thelwell's unique humour in the Beswick models. The first, *An Angel on Horseback*, shows the newest and most naive member of the pony club, with an L plate on her back, about to be taken for a ride by a mount which certainly lacks her innocence. He is sneaking a sly look at the young rider, perhaps contemplating how long it will take to remove her from the saddle. The second, *Kick Start*, shows a frustrated young rider urging on an immovable pony to no avail and in the third, *Pony Express*, another rider struggles to gain control of her runaway.

Left: Design for a reluctant horse resin figure by Harry Sales. Not produced

Below: Sketch by Norman Thelwell

The launch of the Thelwell collection coincided with Royal Doulton's early experiments with a resin body which enabled more complicated poses to be executed with minute detail. Two studies were modelled for this new medium although Harry Sales produced drawings for several others which were never released. The *Studio Sculpture* collection, as the resin models were known, was short lived and examples are now particularly hard to find.

OPPOSITE PAGE

Top left: Kick Start — Grey 2769G, 1983-89

Top right: Pony Express — Bay 2798B, 1983-89

Centre left: Pony Express — Grey 2789G, 1983-89

Centre right: An Angel on Horseback — Grey 2704G, 1982-89

Bottom left: Kick Start — Bay 2769B, 1983-89

Bottom right: An Angel on Horseback — Bay 2704B, 1982-89

86

Thelwell

I Forgive You — Bay SS7, I Forgive You — Grey SS7 and Early Bath — Grey SS12 resin figures, 1984-86

THELWELL

John Beswick backstamp
Designed by Harry Sales

2704G **An Angel on Horseback** (Grey)
Modelled by David Lyttleton
Height: 4½ inches 11.5 cm
Introduced: 1982   Withdrawn: 1989

2704B **An Angel on Horseback** (Bay)
Modelled by David Lyttleton
Height: 4½ inches 11.5 cm
Introduced: 1982   Withdrawn: 1989

2769G **Kick Start** (Grey)
Modelled by David Lyttleton
Height: 3½ inches 8.5 cm
Introduced: 1983   Withdrawn: 1989

2769B **Kick Start** (Bay)
Modelled by David Lyttleton
Height: 3½ inches 8.5 cm
Introduced: 1983   Withdrawn: 1989

2789G **Pony Express** (Grey)
Modelled by David Lyttleton
Height: 4½ inches 11.5 cm
Introduced: 1983   Withdrawn: 1989

2798B **Pony Express** (Bay)
Modelled by David Lyttleton
Height: 4½ inches 11.5 cm
Introduced: 1983   Withdrawn: 1989

Resin models in Studio Sculptures Series
John Beswick adhesive label
Designed by Harry Sales

SS7 **I Forgive You** (Grey or Bay)
Modelled by David Lyttleton
Height: 4 inches 10 cm
Introduced: 1984   Withdrawn: 1986

SS12 **Early Bath** (Grey or Bay)
Modelled by David Lyttleton
Height: 4¾ inches 12 cm
Introduced: 1984   Withdrawn: 1986

Rupert Bear

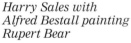
Rupert Bear 2694, 1982-85

R UPERT BEAR was already sixty years old when Harry Sales designed the Beswick range of figures inspired by his adventures. Still a regular feature of the *Daily Express* newspaper, the Rupert stories first appeared in 1920 in a bid to compete with the new cartoon characters in rival publications, in particular Teddy Tail and Pip, Squeak and Wilfred. Mary Tourtel, an established children's illustrator, was told of the quest for a new anthropomorphic character by her husband, the paper's night editor, and she came up with Rupert. He succeeded beyond all expectations, eclipsing all his rivals to become the longest running children's character in a British newspaper.

Although visibly a bear, Rupert has the actions and mannerisms of a small boy. He is fully clothed in distinctive checked trousers, scarf and sweater and has human hands, not paws. He lives in Nutwood with his parents and a host of friends with whom he has the most amazing supernatural adventures. The surreal plots, juxtaposing periods and situations, humans and talking animals, accounted for much of Rupert's popularity. Mary Tourtel often conjured up a Medieval fantasy world for Rupert's adventures with sorcerers, ogres, knights and damsels frequenting 20th century Nutwood without attracting any surprise.

Mary Tourtel's husband supplied the verses which accompanied the serial and his death in 1931 caused more strain in her already demanding schedule. As well as the daily drawings, Rupert appeared in the *Daily Express Children's Annual* from 1930 and the Rupert League was formed in 1932. As Mary's eyesight began to fail, it became obvious that a successor would soon be needed.

*Harry Sales with
Alfred Bestall painting
Rupert Bear*

RUPERT VISITS AN OLD SHOP

"Well, that shop sells old curios,
They might have some old plates, who knows?"

Into the window Rupert stares,
"They do sell plates here," he declares.

"Give me that fragment, little bear,
I've something of this shade! Now, where?"

"Please look, is this it?" Rupert cries.
"Yes," laughs the man. "Bless your sharp eyes."

Lily Duckling thinks quickly. "Yes, perhaps I can help," she quacks. "Your shop-lady said that the colour was only found in old plates. That means you don't want an ordinary china shop. I know this village well. There's an old curiosity shop over there. Why not try it?" "That's a topping idea!" cries Rupert, scampering away. "Yes, this does look a more likely place," he murmurs, "and there are even some plates there, though they are not quite like the one that Mummy broke." The old Curiosity Man invites Rupert into the shop and peers closely at the broken fragment. "I believe I've got something of that shade," he murmurs. "Now where is it?" Crossing to another wall he opens a showcase. All at once Rupert, who has been gazing at the quaint things in the shop, cries out: "Please, look, here's a plate of nearly the same colour!" "Why, bless your sharp eyes, so it is!" laughs the man. "I've kept it for ages and nobody has wanted it, so you may have it cheap."

57

*Page from Rupert Bear
annual, 1975*

Alfred Bestall, a humorous illustrator and regular contributor to *Tatler, The Sketch,* and *Punch* magazines was offered the job in 1935. He soon had to drop all his other commissions, including covers for children's annuals, to concentrate on Rupert as at least 12 drawings were required each week and 80 words of narrative. Bestall injected more humour and ingenuity to the Rupert plots and he drew the character with much more verve and a wider range of facial expressions. The leading personalities created by Mary Tourtel were still easily recognisable, notably Bill Badger, Rupert's oldest friend; Algy Pug, who loves playing practical jokes and the gentle giant Edward Trunk. Bestall introduced characters of his own, including the wealthy Pekinese Pong Ping and the Chinese conjuror, both influenced by the hit musical Chu Chin Chow which started a craze for all things oriental in the 1920s and 30s.

Rupert Bear

Design for Rupert football figures by Harry Sales. Not produced

An annual devoted to Rupert was launched in 1936 and his familiar red sweater and yellow checked scarf and trousers became standard at this date. Mary Tourtel had favoured a more subdued outfit of blue sweater with grey trousers. The Rupert serial continued to appear during the Second World War and a new series of adventure books was launched in 1948. An assistant was brought in to help Bestall with the books but he continued to produce the daily drawings until 1965. He was still supplying the original annual covers and endpapers into his eighties and visited the Beswick factory to discuss his creations with Harry Sales at the age of 90. He expressed himself very pleased with the ceramic interpretations, suggesting only a slight revision to Bill Badger's stripes to improve his expression, and he delighted in painting the eyes on one of the Rupert Bear models.

Sadly Rupert Bear and his friends only remained in production for four years and other ideas for new poses and characters, including a portrait of Edward Trunk, never materialised. Perhaps, the fact that Rupert is relatively unknown overseas affected distribution and sales but one thing is certain, the figures are now very desirable on the secondary market.

Below left: Character references for Pong Ping

Below right: Character references for Bill Badger

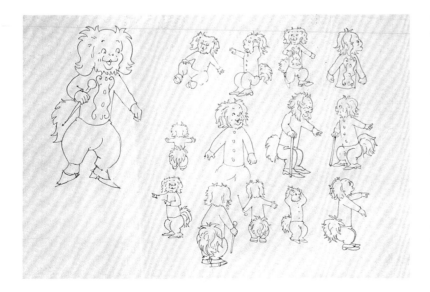

Rupert Bear

Bill Badger 2720, 1982-85

Below: Rupert Bear Snowballing 2779, 1982-85

Algy Pug 2710, 1982-85

Pong Ping 2711, 1982-85

Rupert Bear 2694, 1982-85

RUPERT BEAR

John Beswick backstamp
Designed by Harry Sales

2694 Rupert Bear
Modelled by Graham Tongue
Height: 4¼ inches 10.5 cm
Introduced: 1982   Withdrawn: 1985

2710 Algy Pug
Modelled by Graham Tongue
Height: 4 inches 10 cm
Introduced: 1982   Withdrawn: 1985

2711 Pong Ping
Modelled by Graham Tongue
Height: 4¼ inches 10.5 cm
Introduced: 1982   Withdrawn: 1985

2720 Bill Badger
Modelled by Graham Tongue
Height: 2¾ inches 7 cm
Introduced: 1982   Withdrawn: 1985

2779 Rupert Bear Snowballing
Modelled by Graham Tongue
Height: 4¼ inches 10.5 cm
Introduced: 1982   Withdrawn: 1985

Brambly Hedge

Jill Barklem

'BRAMBLY HEDGE is on the other side of the stream, across the field. If you can find it, and if you look very hard amongst the tangled roots and stems, you may even see a wisp of smoke from a small chimney, or through an open door, a steep flight of stairs deep within the trunk of a tree. For this is the world of the mice of Brambly Hedge'.

The enchanted world of Brambly Hedge was discovered by Jill Barklem whilst she was a student at St Martin's College of Art in the early 1970s. To relieve the tedium of the train journey from her home in Epping Forest to central London she began to fantasise about a community of harvest mice living in the hedgerows on route. She filled countless notebooks with ideas and sketches and studied aspects of life in rural England, such as traditional crafts and herbal remedies. When she married in 1977, her husband David persuaded her to share her imaginary world with others and she showed her research to some publishers. Collins commissioned her to write the first four Brambly Hedge stories, which chart the activities of the mice through the seasons of the year.

The *Spring, Summer, Autumn* and *Winter* stories were published in 1980 and were an immediate success. Readers young and old have been captivated by all the charming details in Jill Barklem's illustrations and enjoy wandering through her pictures, like the mice, and not coming out again for

Right: Wilfred Entertains DBH23, 1990-95

hours. Jill spends hours drawing from nature and taking photographs in Epping Forest to create the settings for her stories and she prowls around her beloved garden, observing the wild life and looking for yet more detail to put into her drawings. Treasures that she has collected on her rambles overflow from the cubby holes of her desk and provide a constant source of reference.

Jill's husband deals in antiques so there are always pieces of old cottage furniture to study and she painstakingly depicts dressers and cupboards crammed with lots of fascinating objects. She has become an expert in country fare, drying herbs, pickling vegetables, making jams and wines and the fruits of her knowledge are shared with the Brambly Hedge mice. Costume details are gleaned from old photographs or paintings of country folk and she has studied the appearance of harvest mice down to the last whisker.

Jill's constant quest for perfection means it can take her at least two weeks to complete one illustration so, not surprisingly, her books are few and far between, with each new title eagerly awaited by her many fans worldwide. To date she has followed the Seasons quartet with *The Secret Staircase* (1983), *The High Hills* (1989), *The Sea Story* (1990) and *Poppy's Babies* (1994). Her books have generated a major merchandising business with the Brambly Hedge mice appearing on clothes, furnishing, stationery, toiletries and many other gift items. In 1980, Royal Doulton secured the rights to reproduce her characters in ceramic and a co-ordinated collection of nursery ware, gift ware and figures was launched in 1983.

Brambly Hedge Savings Books 1990-C

Doulton's Design Managers, Harry Sales and Peter Roberts, spent many hours with Jill, familiarising themselves with her work and discussing their ideas for items as diverse as collectors plates, thimbles, florals and figures. Harry quickly recognised the unique potential of the Brambly Hedge books to inspire collectable figures and remembers: 'When working on the preliminary sketch designs I found myself totally absorbed with the subjects. Jill Barklem's characterisations are superb; each

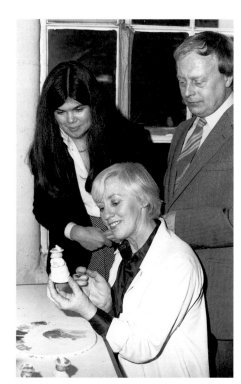

Harry Sales and Jill Barklem watching Brambly Hedge figures being painted

Left: Poppy's Babies illustration by Jill Barklem

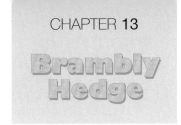

Brambly Hedge

Rare Mr Toadflax with tail in original position DBH10, 1984

line, every expression is absolutely right. In a comparatively short time I felt that I knew the characters — they were so real! Ideas flowed quickly, and I had soon completed sketch designs for the proposed figures having selected suitable characters and poses for our medium. One important feature in the concept was that I chose poses which, when the figures are together, appear to be reacting to one another. I can imagine the fun children and the young at heart will have arranging the figures in conversational situations.'

Peter Roberts, who designed the Brambly Hedge gift ware, has many pleasurable memories of his tour of Epping Forest with Jill and Harry. A sudden rainstorm created a dramatic light which emphasised all the gnarled old trees with their tangled roots and seemed to suggest tiny passages with small doors and windows. 'For a brief moment I felt I was experiencing the real world of Brambly Hedge mice — I half expected to see little mice scurrying about in raincoats!' Peter has endeavoured to recapture this magical experience throughout the Brambly Hedge gift ware

Wilfred Toadflax design by Harry Sales

Illustration from Brambly Hedge Treasury by Jill Barklem

collection which has grown dramatically since 1983. To date there have been around 50 different shapes decorated with scenes derived from Miss Barklem's books and, since Peter's retirement in 1996, the collection continues to grow in the capable hands of Jane James.

The Brambly Hedge figure collection became the responsibility of Design Manager Graham Tongue in 1986 and he chose some delightful subjects from Miss Barklem's

Mrs Apple design by Harry Sales

other books, *The Secret Staircase, The High Hills, The Sea Story* and *Poppy's Babies*. In all, 25 Brambly Hedge characters were introduced before the figure collection was finally withdrawn in 1997. One exceptionally rare model variation exists, showing *Mr Toadflax* (DBH10) with his tail in its original position, and Brambly Hedge fans are hoping to trap this particular mouse. No doubt, in the future, many more collectors will be scurrying around, seeking out the Brambly Hedge mice just as avidly as Mickey or Minnie Mouse.

Left: Mr Toadflax and Old Mrs Eyebright designs by Harry Sales

Brambly Hedge Birthday series, 1987-C

Brambly Hedge

Mr Apple DBH2, 1983-97

Below: Old Vole DBH13, 1985-92

Above centre: Lord Woodmouse DBH4, 1983-97

Above right: Mrs Apple DBH3, 1983-97

Below right: Store Stump Money Box DBH18, 1987-89

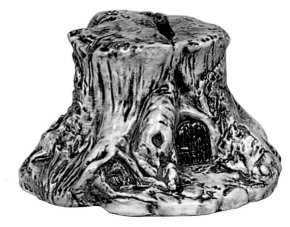

Above: Poppy Eyebright
DBH1, 1983-97

Left: Conker DBH21,
1988-94

Centre: Mrs Toadflax
DBH11, 1985-95

Below left: Mr Saltapple
DBH24, 1993-97

Below right: Mr Toadflax
DBH10, 1984-97

Brambly Hedge

*Right: Primrose
Entertains DBH22,
1990-95*

*Above: Primrose
Woodmouse DBH8, 1983-97*

*Left: Dusty and Baby
DBH26, 1995-97*

*Centre: Dusty Dogwood
DBII6, 1983-97*

*Below: Lily Weaver
DBH19, 1988-93*

Above: Old Mrs Eyebright DBH9, 1984-95

Centre: Flax Weaver DBH20, 1988-93

Right: Lady Woodmouse DBH5, 1983-97

Below left: Wilfred Toadflax DBH7, 1983-97

Below centre: Basil DBH14, 1985-92

Below right: Clover DBH16, 1987-97

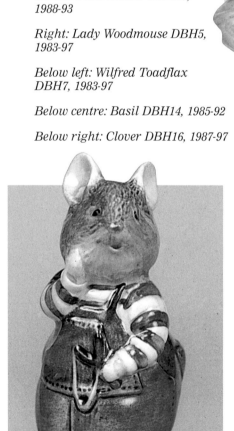

*Catkin DBH12,
1985-94*

*Below centre:
Mrs Crustybread
DBH15, 1987-94*

*Below right:
Mrs Saltapple
DBH25, 1993-97*

*Above: Teasel DBH17,
1987-92*

*Below: Wilfred Entertains
DBH23, 1990-95*

101

BRAMBLY HEDGE

Royal Doulton backstamp
Designed by Harry Sales

DBH1 **Poppy Eyebright**
from *Summer Story*
Modelled by David Lyttleton
Height: 3¹/₄ inches 8 cm
Introduced: 1983   Withdrawn: 1997

DBH2 **Mr Apple**
from *Winter Story*
Modelled by David Lyttleton
Height: 3¹/₄ inches 8 cm
Introduced: 1983   Withdrawn: 1997

DBH3 **Mrs Apple**
from *Winter Story*
Modelled by David Lyttleton
Height: 3¹/₄ inches 8 cm
Introduced: 1983   Withdrawn: 1997

DBH4 **Lord Woodmouse**
from *Autumn Story*
Modelled by David Lyttleton
Height: 3¹/₄ inches 8 cm
Introduced: 1983   Withdrawn: 1997

DBH5 **Lady Woodmouse**
from *Autumn Story*
Modelled by David Lyttleton
Height: 3¹/₄ inches 8 cm
Introduced: 1983   Withdrawn: 1997

DBH6 **Dusty Dogwood**
from *Summer Story*
Modelled by David Lyttleton
Height: 3¹/₄ inches 8 cm
Introduced: 1983   Withdrawn: 1997

DBH7 **Wilfred Toadflax**
from *Spring Story*
Modelled by David Lyttleton
Height: 3¹/₄ inches 8 cm
Introduced: 1983   Withdrawn: 1997

DBH8 **Primrose Woodmouse**
from *Autumn Story*
Modelled by David Lyttleton
Height: 3¹/₄ inches 8 cm
Introduced: 1983   Withdrawn: 1997

DBH9 **Old Mrs Eyebright**
from *Summer Story*
Modelled by David Lyttleton
Height: 3¹/₄ inches 8 cm
Introduced: 1984   Withdrawn: 1995

DBH10 **Mr Toadflax**
from *Spring Story*
Modelled by David Lyttleton
Height: 3¹/₄ inches 8 cm
Introduced: 1984   Withdrawn: 1997
The tail of this figure was remodelled
shortly after its introduction

DBH11 **Mrs Toadflax**
from *Winter Story*
Modelled by David Lyttleton
Height: 3¹/₄ inches 8 cm
Introduced: 1985   Withdrawn: 1995

DBH12 **Catkin**
from *Winter Story*
Modelled by David Lyttleton
Height: 3¹/₄ inches 8 cm
Introduced: 1985   Withdrawn: 1994

DBH13 **Old Vole**
from *Summer Story*
Modelled by David Lyttleton
Height: 3¹/₄ inches 8 cm
Introduced: 1985   Withdrawn: 1992

DBH14 **Basil**
from *Summer Story*
Modelled by David Lyttleton
Height: 3¹/₄ inches 8 cm
Introduced: 1985   Withdrawn: 1992

DBH15 **Mrs Crustybread**
from *Spring Story*
Modelled by Ted Chawner
Height: 3¹/₄ inches 8 cm
Introduced: 1987   Withdrawn: 1994

DBH16 **Clover**
from *Winter Story*
Modelled by Graham Tongue
Height: 3¹/₄ inches 8 cm
Introduced: 1987   Withdrawn: 1997

DBH17 **Teasel**
from *Winter Story*
Modelled by Ted Chawner
Height: 3¹/₄ inches 8 cm
Introduced: 1987   Withdrawn: 1992

DBH18 **Store Stump Money Box**
Modelled by Martyn Alcock
Height: 3¹/₄ inches 8 cm
Introduced: 1987   Withdrawn: 1989

DBH19 **Lily Weaver**
from *The High Hills*
Modelled by Ted Chawner
Height: 3¹/₄ inches 8 cm
Introduced: 1988   Withdrawn: 1993

DBH20 **Flax Weaver**
from *The High Hills*
Modelled by Ted Chawner
Height: 3¹/₄ inches 8 cm
Introduced: 1988   Withdrawn: 1993

DBH21 **Conker**
from *Summer Story*
Modelled by Ted Chawner
Height: 3¹/₄ inches 8 cm
Introduced: 1988   Withdrawn: 1994

DBH22 Primrose Entertains
from *The Secret Staircase*
Modelled by Alan Maslankowski
Height: 3¼ inches 8 cm
Introduced: 1990   Withdrawn: 1995

DBH23 Wilfred Entertains
from *The Secret Staircase*
Modelled by Alan Maslankowski
Height: 3¼ inches 8 cm
Introduced: 1990   Withdrawn: 1995

DBH24 Mr Saltapple
from *The Sea Story*
Modelled by Warren Platt
Height: 2¼ inches 5.5 cm
Introduced: 1993   Withdrawn: 1997

DBH25 Mrs Saltapple
from *The Sea Story*
Modelled by Warren Platt
Height: 3½ inches 8.5 cm
Introduced: 1993   Withdrawn: 1997

DBH26 Dusty and Baby
from *Poppy's Babies*
Modelled by Martyn Alcock
Height: 2¾ inches 7 cm
Introduced: 1995   Withdrawn: 1997

Royal Doulton®
MR. SALTAPPLE
D.B.H. 24
FROM THE BRAMBLY HEDGE
GIFT COLLECTION
© JILL BARKLEM 199?

BRAMBLY HEDGE GIFT WARE

Royal Doulton backstamp
Designed by Peter Roberts after illustrations
by Jill Barklem

WALL PLATES

Four Seasons 1983 – C
Spring
Summer
Autumn
Winter

Midwinter's Eve
The Snowball 1984 – 1991
The Discovery 1985 – 1991
Candlelight Supper 1986 – 1991
The Entertainment 1987 – 1991

Midwinter's Eve 1991 for Lawleys by Post

The Interiors 1986 – 1997
The Store Stump
The Dairy
Crabapple Cottage
Old Oak Palace

Occasions
The Birthday 1987 – C
The Wedding 1987 – C
The Engagement 1989 – 1997
Merry Midwinter 1995 – 1997

The Secret Staircase 1990 – 1996
The Palace Kitchen
The Forgotten Room
The Grand Bathroom
The Great Hall

**Primrose's Adventure
1991 – 1995**
Where's Primrose
The Search Party
The Adventure
Safe at Last

Surprise Outing 1993 – 1997
The Plan
The Meeting
The Invitation
The Outing

The Picnic 1990 – 1993

Poppy's Babies 1997 – C

Annual
Spring Story Year plate 1996
Summer Story Year plate 1997

GIFT WARE AND TEA WARE

8 inch wall plate 1983 – C
Thimble 1983 – C
Beaker 1984 – C
Teacup and saucer 1984 – C
Children's teacup and saucer 1990 – 1993
6 inch tea plate 1984 – C
Teapot 1987 – C
Sugar bowl 1987 – C
Cream jug 1987 – C
Coaster 1989 – C
Gainsborough vase 1990 – 1997
Gainsborough vase S/S 1991 – 1993
Sandwich tray 1989 – 1993
Trinket box 1990 – C
Clock 1989 – C

Brambly Hedge

Savings book 1990 – C
Egg cup 1990 – C
Bread and butter plate 1990 – C
Coffee pot 1990 – 1997
Fruit saucer 1990 – C
Marmalade pot 1990 – 1997
Regal tray 1990 – C
Lamp 1990 – 1991
Dorothy box 1990 – C
Clover box 1990 – 1992
Petal bowl 1990 – 1992
Footed bowl 1990 – 1992
Photograph frame 1992 – 1995
Powder bowl 1991 – 1995
Pin tray 1991 – 1993

Posy vase 1991 – 1994
Ring stand 1991 – 1993
Ewer and basin 1991 – 1997
Hinged box 1992 – 1995
Candlestick 1995 – 1997

Miniatures
Miniature teapot, cream jug and sugar bowl
    1987 – 1997
Miniature teacup, saucer and plate 1987 – 1997
Miniature beaker 1990 – 1993
Miniature trinket box 1990 – 1992

Florals
Spring Posy 1983 – 1989
Summer Bouquet 1983 – 1989
Autumn Basket 1983 – 1989
Winter Hollow 1983 – 1989

Jewellery
Silver pendant 1984 – 1986
Gold pendant 1984 – 1986

Thimbles 1984 – 1992

Selection of Four Seasons gift ware – Winter Story

Selection of Four Seasons gift ware – Autumn Story

The Snowman

Raymond Briggs

THE SNOWMAN melted the hearts of millions of TV viewers when his story was first screened at Christmas time in 1982. This enchanting film about a little boy called James, who builds a snowman that comes to life, was based on the best selling book by Raymond Briggs. A successful author and illustrator, Briggs has published many books for children since he graduated from the Wimbledon and Slade schools of art in 1957. He has twice won the prestigious Kate Greenaway medal, notably for *Father Christmas* in 1973, the first book in which he adopted the distinctive strip cartoon format without words which he used so successfully in *The Snowman* of 1978.

There are only a few words of introduction in the film version of the story which unfolds to evocative music as James and the Snowman explore each other's worlds. There are many comical scenes in James' house when the Snowman dresses up in the father's clothes and recuperates in the deep freeze, which is more to his liking than the fire and cooker. When he becomes homesick for the land of the snowmen, they fly there together to the strains of the haunting theme song 'Walking in the Air' and arrive in time for a jolly party, with lots of music and dancing. After meeting Father Christmas, they return home but James awakes next morning to find his Snowman has melted away and his bitter disappointment brings tears to the eyes of viewers young and old.

Within a few years of the film debut, *The Snowman* was appearing on a wide range of products from stationery to textiles and Royal Doulton secured the license for interpreting his exploits in ceramic. Raymond Briggs followed the development of his character with interest and was impressed with how well the various licensees translated the Snowman into various mediums. The Royal Doulton studios were no exception —

Right: Snowman illustration by Raymond Briggs

'They really got into the spirit of the thing' he said 'Everything they have done is marvellous'.

It was quite a challenge to recreate the soft crayon effect of Raymond Briggs' original drawings in ceramic but, after much experimentation, Design Manager Peter Roberts succeeded admirably with his range of decorative gift ware. Scenes from both the film and the book were used on a variety of bone china items, including wall plates, beakers, trinket boxes, a salt and pepper set and a money bank. New shapes were developed especially for the range, notably the first ever Doulton mobile, a set of Christmas tree ornaments and the ingenious *Build a Snowman* sets, one comprising a stacking egg cup and saucer and the other a mug, plate and cereal bowl. The picture plates have proved to be the most popular with collectors and there are five in the series, two of which were short lived and so are harder to find, *Snowman Rides a Motorbike* and *Snowman's Visit*.

Translating the stocky, simplified shapes of the *Snowman* illustrations into three dimensional figures was an even more daunting task for Design Manager Harry Sales but, working closely with Raymond Briggs, he introduced additional curves to the contours of the figures in order to create lively poses, which capture comical or enchanted moments from the tale. The figures were designed to interact with each other, thus in the first group *James* (DS1) can look up in wonder as his creation comes to life in *The Snowman* (DS2) or he can admire his father's clothes on the *Stylish Snowman* (DS3). The fourth figure shows them together in

Left: Bass Drummer Snowman DS9, 1987-93

Below: Design for Snowman with Balloons by Harry Sales, not produced and Cowboy Snowman DS6, 1986-92

The Snowman

an affectionate embrace *Thank You Snowman (*DS4).

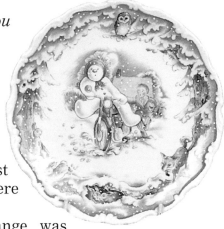

In the second group of figures launched in 1986, Harry Sales introduced some of the revellers from the snowmen's party, including *Highland Snowman* (DS7), *Cowboy Snowman* (DS6) and *Lady Snowman* (DS8). The last two are now amongst the hardest to find as they were withdrawn before the others in 1992.

From 1987 until 1990, the range was developed by the new Design Manager Graham Tongue and, with modeller Warren Platt, he was responsible for the delightful *Snowman Band (*DS9-17) and the group of snowmen playing in the snow (DS20-23). Of these, the *Snowman Skiing* (DS21) remained in the range for less than two years and it now commands the highest price in the marketplace.

There are nineteen figures to collect in total plus two musical boxes adorned with figures (DS5 and DS18) and a money bank modelled in the form of a snowman (DS19). In 1994, Royal Doulton USA commissioned a miniature *Snowman* character jug (D6972) which was only available for one year so no doubt it will also prove elusive in the future. Since the withdrawal of the entire *Snowman* range at the end of 1994 interest in the figures has grown dramatically and prices have been snowballing so the lucky children who received *Snowman* figures in their Christmas stockings over the years now have a valuable collection.

Right: Snowman Rides a Motorbike plate, 1987-91

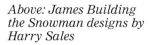

Above: James Building the Snowman designs by Harry Sales

Right: Build a Snowman sets, 1985-93

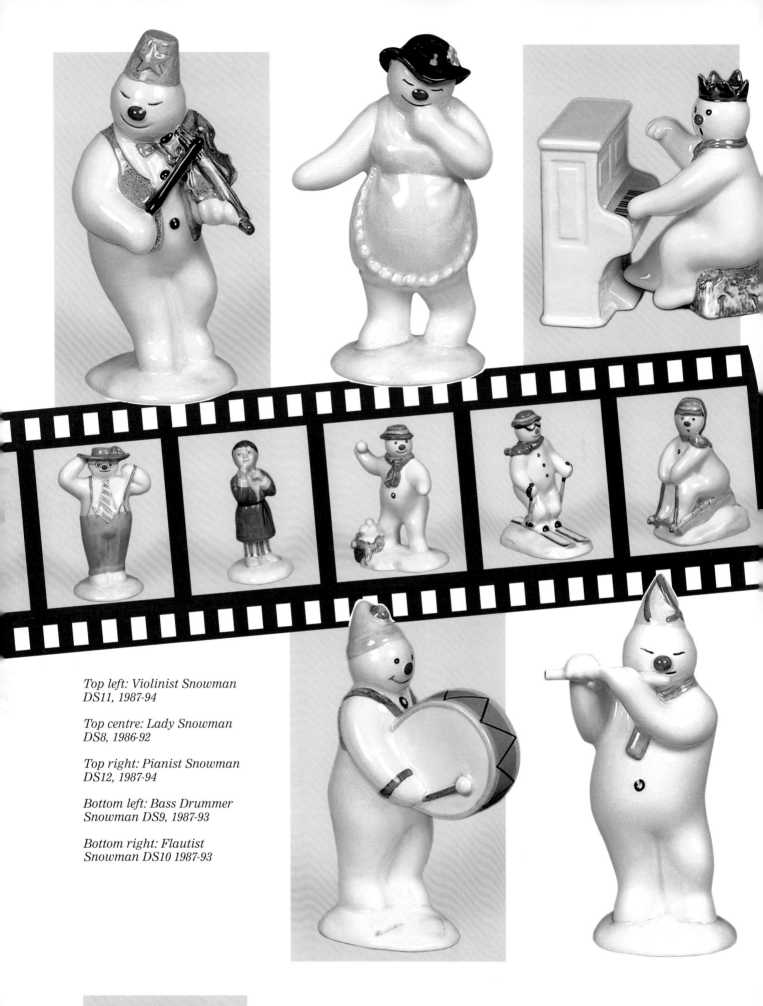

*Top left: Violinist Snowman
DS11, 1987-94*

*Top centre: Lady Snowman
DS8, 1986-92*

*Top right: Pianist Snowman
DS12, 1987-94*

*Bottom left: Bass Drummer
Snowman DS9, 1987-93*

*Bottom right: Flautist
Snowman DS10 1987-93*

108

*Top left: Cellist Snowman
DS17, 1988-94*

*Top right: Drummer
Snowman DS15, 1988-94*

*Bottom left: Cymbal
Player Snowman DS14,
1988-93*

*Bottom right: Building
the Snowman DS23,
1990-94*

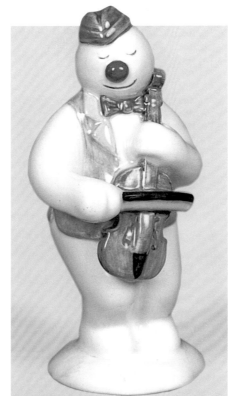

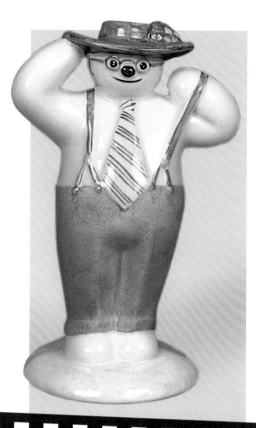

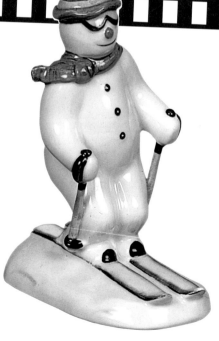

Top left: The Snowballing Snowman DS22, 1990-94

Top centre: James DS1, 1985-93

Top right: Stylish Snowman DS3, 1985-93

Bottom left: The Snowman Skiing DS21, 1990-91

Bottom right: The Snowman Tobogganing DS20, 1990-94

The Snowman

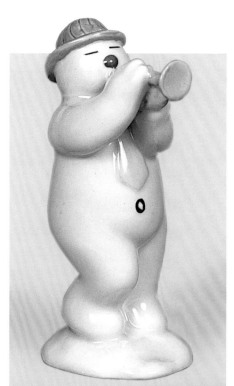

*Top left: Trumpeter
Snowman DS16, 1988-93*

*Top right: Thank You
Snowman DS4, 1985-94*

*Bottom left: Snowman
Money Box DS19, 1990-94*

*Bottom centre: Snowman
Musical Box DS18, 1988-90*

*Bottom right: Snowman
Magic Musical Box DS5,
1985-94*

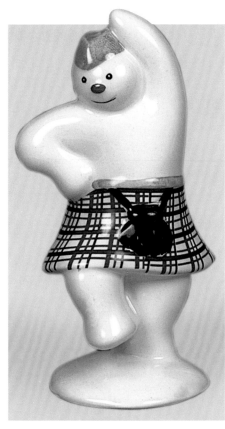

The Snowman DS2, 1985-94　　*Cowboy Snowman DS6, 1986-92*　　*Highland Snowman DS7, 1986-93*

THE SNOWMAN

Royal Doulton backstamp
Designed by Harry Sales

DS1　James
Modelled by David Lyttleton
Height: 3¾ inches 9.5 cm
Introduced: 1985   Withdrawn: 1993

DS2　The Snowman
Modelled by David Lyttleton
Height: 5 inches 12.5 cm
Introduced: 1985   Withdrawn: 1994

DS3　Stylish Snowman
Modelled by David Lyttleton
Height: 5 inches 12.5 cm
Introduced: 1985   Withdrawn: 1993

DS4　Thank You Snowman
Modelled by David Lyttleton
Height: 5 inches 12.5 cm
Introduced: 1985   Withdrawn: 1994

DS5　Snowman Magic Musical Box
This features the figure DS2
and plays 'Walking in the Air'
Height: 8 inches 20.5 cm
Introduced: 1985   Withdrawn: 1994

DS6　Cowboy Snowman
Modelled by David Lyttleton
Height: 5 inches 12.5 cm
Introduced: 1986   Withdrawn: 1992

DS7　Highland Snowman
Modelled by David Lyttleton
Height: 5 inches 12.5 cm
Introduced: 1986   Withdrawn: 1993

DS8　Lady Snowman
Modelled by David Lyttleton
Height: 5 inches 12.5 cm
Introduced: 1986   Withdrawn: 1992

The Snowman

Designed by Graham Tongue

DS9   **Bass Drummer Snowman**
Modelled by Warren Platt
Height: 5½ inches 13.5 cm
Introduced: 1987   Withdrawn: 1993

DS10   **Flautist Snowman**
Modelled by Warren Platt
Height: 5½ inches 13.5 cm
Introduced: 1987   Withdrawn: 1993

DS11   **Violinist Snowman**
Modelled by Warren Platt
Height: 5¼ inches 13 cm
Introduced: 1987   Withdrawn: 1994

DS12   **Pianist Snowman**
Modelled by Warren Platt
Height: 5 inches 12.5 cm
Introduced: 1987   Withdrawn: 1994

DS13   **Snowman's Piano**
Modelled by Warren Platt
Height: 5 inches 12.5 cm
Introduced: 1987   Withdrawn: 1994

DS14   **Cymbal Player Snowman**
Modelled by Warren Platt
Height: 5¼ inches 13 cm
Introduced: 1988   Withdrawn: 1993

DS15   **Drummer Snowman**
Modelled by Warren Platt
Height: 5¾ inches 14.5 cm
Introduced: 1988   Withdrawn: 1994

DS16   **Trumpeter Snowman**
Modelled by Warren Platt
Height: 5 inches 12.5 cm
Introduced: 1988   Withdrawn: 1993

DS17   **Cellist Snowman**
Modelled by Warren Platt
Height: 5¼ inches 13 cm
Introduced: 1988   Withdrawn: 1993

DS18   **Snowman Musical Box**
This features the figure DS7
and plays 'Blue Bells of Scotland'
Height: 8 inches 20.5 cm
Introduced: 1988   Withdrawn: 1990

DS19   **The Snowman Money Box**
Modelled by Graham Tongue
Height: 8½ inches 21.5 cm
Introduced: 1990   Withdrawn: 1994

DS20   **The Snowman Tobogganing**
Modelled by Warren Platt
Height: 5 inches 12.5 cm
Introduced: 1990   Withdrawn: 1994

DS21   **The Snowman Skiing**
Modelled by Warren Platt
Height: 5 inches 12.5 cm
Introduced: 1990   Withdrawn: 1991

DS22   **The Snowballing Snowman**
Modelled by Warren Platt
Height: 5 inches 12.5 cm
Introduced: 1990   Withdrawn: 1994

DS23   **Building the Snowman**
Modelled by Warren Platt
Height: 4 inches 10 cm
Introduced: 1990   Withdrawn: 1994

D6972   **The Snowman Character Jug (Version 1)**
Modelled by Martyn Alcock
Height: 2¾ inches 7 cm
Introduced: 1994 only exclusively
for the USA

*Snowman Character Jug
(Version 1) D6972, 1994 only*

The Snowman

SNOWMAN NURSERY AND GIFT WARE

Royal Doulton backstamp
Designed by Peter Roberts after illustrations
by Raymond Briggs

Wall plates
Snowman Christmas Cake 1985 – 1994
Walking in the Air 1985 – 1994
Dance of the Snowman 1986 – 1994
Snowman Rides a Motorbike 1987 – 1991
Snowman's Visit 1990 – 1994

Beakers
Walking in the Air 1985 – 1994
The Party 1985 – 1994
Building the Snowman 1985 – 1994
Playful Snowman 1985 – 1994
Into the Forest 1989 – 1994
Beaker with soft toy 1987 – 1991

Nursery ware
Hug a mug with 1 handle — snowman
     musicians 1988 – 1994
Build a Snowman set 2 pieces 1985 – 1993
Build a Snowman set 3 pieces 1985 – 1993

Gift ware
Mobile 7 pieces 1985 – 1993
Money ball — singing snowman 1985 – 1994
Money ball — 'Christmas Celebration'
     1991 – 1993
Round box — balloons 1985 – 1993
Oval box — Highland fling 1985 – 1993
Christmas Tree ornaments (4) 1989 – 1993
Coaster 1987 – 1993
Clock 1989 – 1994
Ginger jar L/S 1990 – 1991
Ginger jar S/S 1990 – 1991
Savings book 1990 – 1994
Salt and pepper set 1990 – 1991

Gift sets
Party time set 1986 – 1994
Comprising 6 inch plate, cup and saucer

Children's set 1989 – 1994
Comprising hug-a-mug with 1 handle and
     cereal bowl

Children's set 1989 – 1994
Comprising 8 inch plate, hug-a-mug with 1
     handle and cereal bowl

Christmas Celebration set 1991 – 1994
Comprising baby plate and hug-a-mug with 2
handles

Miniature tea set 1990 – 1994
Comprising plate, cup and saucer

Above: Snowman salt and pepper set, 1990-91

Below: Selection of Snowman nursery ware

The Wind in the Willows

Christina Thwaites

Right: Toad as Washerwoman by Francis Pope, c1910

'I LOVE these little people, be kind to them' was Kenneth Grahame's request to the illustrator Ernest Shepard as he set out to visualise Toad, Ratty, Mole and Badger for one of the best known illustrated editions of *The Wind in the Willows* in 1930. When the book was first published in 1908, there was only a frontispiece but subsequently many artists have endeavoured to do justice to Grahame's immortal characters, from book illustrators to ceramic modellers to cartoon animators.

Toad was the hero of a long-running bedtime story which Grahame began relating to his young son Alastair, nicknamed 'Mouse', when he was four years old. The tales were inspired by the animals they met on their river bank walks and their adventures unfolded over the next four years, latterly in letter form when father and son were apart for the summer. Grahame, who was already well known as a writer, was persuaded to present the tales to some publishers. The character of the irrepressible, bombastic Toad, crying 'poop poop' as he terrorised the countryside in his motorcar, was already well developed in the letters but his riverbank friends needed to be fleshed out, resulting in the irascible Mr Badger with a soft heart beneath his gruff exterior, the hearty, down to earth Ratty and the timid Mole.

The initial reaction to the finished manuscript was that the story was too fantastic and not at all what was expected from the author of *The Golden Age* (1893) and *Dream Days* (1898) two of Grahame's highly successful books about childhood. Nevertheless *The Wind in the Willows* was published eventually to mixed reviews. Amongst the first fans were President Roosevelt, who arranged for the book's publication in the US, and the author Arnold Bennett who wrote, 'The book is an urbane exercise in irony at the expense of the English character and of mankind. It is entirely successful'. Although Grahame always refused to admit the book's deeper meaning, most adult readers believe it to be allegorical and even autobiographical. Toad has been identified as young 'Mouse', particularly in his tendency to exult his exploits, and the Wild Wood is thought to represent the cunning and treachery of the City where Grahame worked unhappily as a banker.

Whatever the book's true meaning, Grahame's characters are essentially human beings represented in the shape of various animals as an expression of their personalities. This is true also of the first two Royal Doulton figures which are basically humans with toad heads. They were modelled in salt glazed stoneware by one of the Lambeth studio's leading artists, Francis Pope, and they depict a very smug Mr Toad in pinstripes and tails and a haughty Toad disguised as a washerwoman in order to escape from prison. The exact date of these impressive figures is not recorded but they are amongst the earliest interpretations of the hero from *The Wind in the Willows*. Unfortunately they are both very rare, only two examples having come to light.

The Wind in the Willows gradually grew in popularity and, by the time Grahame died in 1932, it had been reprinted many times and was being hailed as a children's classic. Mr Toad's adventures reached an even wider audience after the stage adaptation by A A Milne was first performed in 1930. Milne was a devoted fan of the book and acknowledged its influence on his own bedtime stories about *Winnie the Pooh*. His *Toad of Toad Hall*, a children's play with music, was a great success in its own right and for many years was regularly performed at Christmas time in London. By

Autumn in the Wild Wood plate design by Christina Thwaites, 1987

Designs for thimbles with Badger, Mole, Ratty and Toad by Christina Thwaites, 1987

The Wind in the Willows

Designs for Badger, Mole, Toad and Ratty by Harry Sales

the late 1930s, Walt Disney was considering an animated feature film of *The Wind in the Willows* although it was not produced until 1949 in a much shortened form along with *The Legend of Sleepy Hollow* as *The Adventures of Ichabod and Mr Toad*.

Even with so many varied interpretations from the past, new artists have continued to be inspired by the adventures of Grahame's riverbank community. In the early 1980s, Christina Thwaites, a young children's book illustrator from Hampshire,

The Wind in the Willows illustration by Christina Thwaites

was commissioned to produce a series of *The Wind in the Willows* wall plates for the Royal Doulton and Royal Albert ranges. Her delicate whimsical style, combining naturalism with fantasy, created a new look for the classic tale. Four episodes were chosen for the first plates, which were launched in 1984, and these were followed in 1987 by seven more. Beakers and afternoon tea sets were also made along with four thimbles depicting the leading characters *Toad, Mole, Ratty* and *Badger.*

At the same time as the gift ware range was being developed, Design Manager Harry Sales was working on a collection of little figures, based on Christina Thwaites illustrations but with some modifications, notably Mole's dressing gown. His designs were modelled by David Lyttleton and went into production with the Royal Albert backstamp in 1987. Harry also worked on designs for the two little hedgehog characters who lost their way in the Wild Wood but they were not developed after he left the Beswick studio. Instead Alan Maslankowski modelled figures of *Portly,* the little otter who goes missing and *Weasel,* the gamekeeper who usurped Toad Hall. These two are now the hardest to find as they were made for only two years before the entire collection was withdrawn in 1989.

Below: Hedgehog designs by Harry Sales.
Not produced

The Wind in the Willows

Above: Ratty 2941, 1987-89

Above centre: Mole 2939, 1987-89

Above right: Toad 2942, 1987-89

Left: Badger 2940, 1987-89

Above: Portly 3065, 1988-89

Right: Weasel 3076, 1988-89

THE WIND IN THE WILLOWS

Royal Albert backstamp
Designed by Harry Sales

2939   **Mole**
Modelled by David Lyttleton
Height: 3 inches 7.5 cm
Introduced: 1987   Withdrawn: 1989

2940   **Badger**
Modelled by David Lyttleton
Height: 3 inches 7.5 cm
Introduced: 1987   Withdrawn: 1989

2941   **Ratty**
Modelled by David Lyttleton
Height: 3³/₄ inches 9.5 cm
Introduced: 1987   Withdrawn: 1989

2942   **Toad**
Modelled by David Lyttleton
Height: 3³/₄ inches 9.5 cm
Introduced: 1987   Withdrawn: 1989

3065   **Portly**
Modelled by Alan Maslankowski
Height: 2³/₄ inches 7 cm
Introduced: 1988   Withdrawn: 1989

3076   **Weasel**
Modelled by Alan Maslankowski
Height: 4 inches 10 cm
Introduced: 1988   Withdrawn: 1989

Below: Wall plates – The Carol Singers, Autumn in the Wild Wood, The Picnic and Portly's Return

THE WIND IN THE WILLOWS GIFT WARE

Royal Doulton backstamp
Commissioned by Lawleys by Post and designed by Peter Roberts after illustrations by Christina Thwaites

Wall plates
Badger's House 1984 – 1989
Preparation for the Boating Season 1984 – 1989
Ratty and Mole go Boating 1984 – 1989
Rambling in the Wild Wood 1984 – 1989
Return of Ulysses 1987 – 1989
The Open Road 1987 – 1989
Badger's Party 1987 – 1989

Royal Albert backstamp
Designed by Peter Roberts after illustrations by Christina Thwaites

Wall plates
Portly's Return 1987 – 1989
The Picnic 1987 – 1989
Autumn in the Wild Wood 1987 – 1989
The Carol Singers 1987 – 1989

Beakers
Portly's Return 1987 – 1989
The Picnic 1987 – 1989
Autumn in the Wild Wood 1987 – 1989
The Carol Singers 1987 – 1989

Afternoon Tea Set
Comprising 6 inch plate, teacup and saucer

Portly's Return 1987 – 1989
The Picnic 1987 – 1989
Autumn in the Wild Wood 1987 – 1989
The Carol Singers 1987 – 1989

Thimbles
Mole 1987 – 1989
Toad 1987 – 1989
Ratty 1987 – 1989
Badger 1987 – 1989

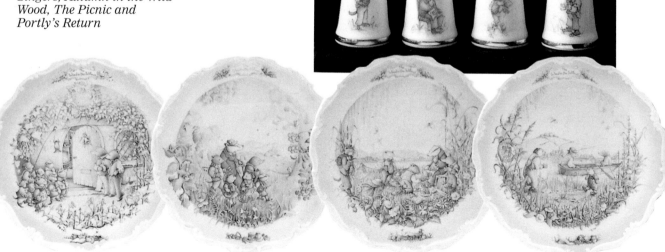

Thunderbirds

THROUGHOUT THE 1960s, Gerry and Sylvia Anderson thrilled young TV audiences with their Supermarionation shows, such as *Stingray, Captain Scarlet* and *Thunderbirds*. These action-packed adventures, starring puppet heroes and villains, were renowned for their amazing futuristic settings and innovative special effects. Many of the series have been repeated for younger generations and some, like *Thunderbirds*, have now achieved cult status. Nostalgic adults avidly watched the recent re-run of 32 *Thunderbirds* episodes and some have become collectors of original costumes and accessories from the show.

In response to this enthusiasm, the Beswick studio introduced six busts of the most popular *Thunderbirds* characters in 1992. Modelled by Bill Harper, they were sold through Lawleys by Post in a limited edition of 2,500. The busts are effective likenesses of the puppets from International Rescue, a secret organisation ready to help the rest of humanity in the year 2063. The main assets of this fighting force, staffed by Jeff Tracy and his five sons, are its five supercraft known as the Thunderbirds.

Scott Tracy, the pilot of Thunderbird 1, is responsible for assessing trouble and

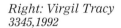

Right: Virgil Tracy
3345,1992

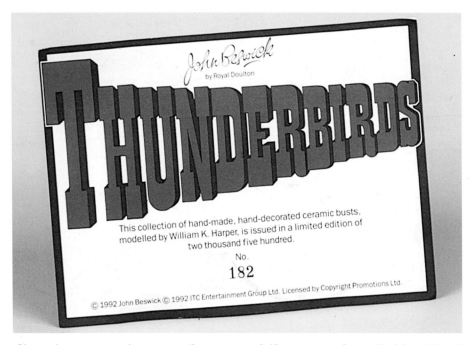

Parker 3346, 1992

directing operations on the spot whilst staunch, reliable *Virgil Tracy* is the pilot of Thunderbird 2, the cargo vehicle which transports equipment to the site of a rescue. It was *Brains,* the scientific wiz, who invented the Thunderbirds and he constantly comes up with new ideas for gadgets to help defeat *The Hood,* arch-enemy of the International Rescue. *Lady Penelope,* the elegant London agent, adds glamour to the show as she is driven around in her shocking pink Rolls Royce, licence plate FAB 1, by her chauffeur *Parker,* a cockney ex-criminal with plenty of useful skills. Together they make a colourful and collectable crew — 'F.A.B.' as Scott Tracy would say.

Brains 3339, 1992

Left: Scott Tracy on Thunderbird Five

Thunderbirds

Top right: Scott Tracy 3344, 1992

Centre: The Hood 3348, 1992

Bottom left: Lady Penelope 3337, 1992

Bottom right: Virgil Tracy 3345, 1992

THUNDERBIRDS

John Beswick backstamp

3337   **Lady Penelope Bust**
Modelled by Bill Harper
Height: 4 inches 10 cm
Introduced: 1992
Commissioned by Lawleys by Post
in a limited edition of 2,500

3339   **Brains Bust**
Modelled by Bill Harper
Height: 4 inches 10 cm
Introduced: 1992
Commissioned by Lawleys by Post
in a limited edition of 2,500

3344   **Scott Tracy Bust**
Modelled by Bill Harper
Height: 4 inches 10 cm
Introduced: 1992
Commissioned by Lawleys by Post
in a limited edition of 2,500

3345   **Virgil Tracy Bust**
Modelled by Bill Harper
Height: 4 inches 10 cm
Introduced: 1992
Commissioned by Lawleys by Post
in a limited edition of 2,500

3346   **Parker Bust**
Modelled by Bill Harper
Height: 4 inches 10 cm
Introduced: 1992
Commissioned by Lawleys by Post
in a limited edition of 2,500

3348   **The Hood Bust**
Modelled by Bill Harper
Height: 4 inches 10 cm
Introduced: 1992
Commissioned by Lawleys by Post
in a limited edition of 2,500

The Dandy and The Beano

OPPOSITE PAGE

*Dennis and Gnasher
D7005, and Desperate Dan
D7006, 1995 – C*

*Dennis the Menace comic
illustration*

THE DANDY comic was launched in 1937 by D C Thomson of Dundee and became an immediate success. The new half-tabloid format made it easier to handle and the action was explained in speech bubbles rather than conventional lines of text making the paper simple to read. Children responded to the tough boisterous humour which was new to comics at the time and laughed at the exploits of outrageous characters, such as *Desperate Dan*. Created by Albert Barnes, this Wild West character was drawn for the first thirty years by Dudley D Watkins, who also visualised other comic stars including Biffo the Bear and Lord Snooty and his Pals. Desperate Dan possesses great strength which causes havoc in his home town of Cactusville, for instance a sneeze can bend lamp-posts! He shaves with a blow lamp, the only thing that will remove his cast iron bristles, and sparks fly in the process! His gargantuan appetite is also a source of humour, his favourite meal being cow pie, made by his Aunt Aggy, washed down with Owl Hoot juice.

look out, world...

Although many parents considered *The Dandy* crude, D C Thomson had developed the type of comic that children really wanted to read and at twopence a copy it could be purchased with pocket money. A companion comic, *The Beano,* was introduced in 1938 and a host of new characters kept the young customers amused. Amongst the favourites over the years have been Roger the Dodger, Minnie the Minx, Biffo the Bear and the Bash Street Kids.

Dennis the Menace, the 'world's wildest boy' created by David Law, made his debut in *The Beano* in 1951 and ousted Biffo the Bear from the front page position in 1974. Inevitably, he gets into all sorts of mischief with his peashooter and his faithful dog Gnasher, a scribble of black fur and sharp teeth. Apparently Gnasher is actually a very rare Abyssinian Wire-Haired Tripe Hound with a taste for trouser legs! Dennis is the undisputed master of mayhem and children love all his pranks, which they dream of doing but would not dare. Instead they can join the Dennis the Menace fan club (including Gnasher's fang club!) and win look-alike jerseys in red and black stripes by sending in jokes, photographs and cartoons.

Minnie the Minx, introduced by Leo Baxendale in 1953, is a female equivalent of Dennis the Menace, even wearing the same red and black jersey. Boisterous and egotistical, she specialises in pulverising boys. Baxendale also created the anarchic Bash Street Kids, which became a full page cartoon in the Beano in 1956. It is constant chaos in the Bash Street School as the unruly kids, led by Danny, dream up schemes to plague the teacher and Cuthbert, the class swot. None of the characters are blessed with good looks but Plug with his protruding mouth and ears is particularly bizarre.

The Dandy and *The Beano* are the longest running, most widely read British comics and generations of children have grown up with the weekly strip cartoons, summer specials and Christmas annuals. In 1995, Royal Doulton paid tribute to the comic heroes, Desperate Dan and Dennis the Menace, by portraying them as large size character jugs and the following year they were issued in a small size, together with portraits of Minnie the Minx and Plug. This is the first time cartoon characters have been represented in this way and it opens up lots of possibilities for the future.

Gnasher comic illustration

Desperate Dan comic illustration

The Dandy and The Beano

Plug D7035, 1996-C

*Top right:
Dennis and
Gnasher D7005
& D7033,
1995-C*

*Minnie the Minx
D7036, 1996-C*

*Desperate Dan D7006,
1995-C*

THE DANDY AND THE BEANO

Royal Doulton backstamp

D7005 **Dennis and Gnasher**
Character jug L/S
Modelled by Simon Ward
Height: 7 inches 17.5 cm
Introduced: 1995   Still in production

D7006 **Desperate Dan**
Character jug L/S
Modelled by Simon Ward
Height: 7 inches 17.5 cm
Introduced: 1995   Still in production

D7033 **Dennis and Gnasher**
Character jug S/S
Modelled by Simon Ward
Height: 4 inches 10 cm
Introduced: 1996   Still in production

D7034 **Desperate Dan**
Character jug S/S
Modelled by Simon Ward
Height: 4 inches 10 cm
Introduced: 1996   Still in production

D7035 **Plug**
Character jug S/S
Modelled by Simon Ward
Height: 4 inches 10 cm
Introduced: 1996   Still in production

D7036 **Minnie the Minx**
Character jug S/S
Modelled by Simon Ward
Height: 4 inches 10 cm
Introduced: 1996   Still in production

Tom & Jerry

TOM & JERRY made their debut in *Puss Gets the Boot* at the MGM studios in 1940 and they have been chasing each other ever since to the delight of audiences young and old. They have starred in over 200 cartoons, which have been released all over the world, and they are the proud winners of eight prestigious Academy Awards.

Tom & Jerry were the creation of William Hanna and Joseph Barbera, who joined Metro-Goldwyn-Mayer's new animation studio in 1937. Hanna had no formal training in art but, in 1931, his love of cartoons took him to the new Hollywood animation company, Harman and Ising, where he learned the ropes, in between making coffee and sweeping the floor! He was involved in tracing and painting the first Looney Tunes and Merrie Melodies before specialising in writing.

Joseph Barbera started his career as a banker but he spent more of his time drawing and selling cartoons to magazines so he eventually entered the New York animation industry. He worked at the Van Beuren Studio and then at Paul Terry's before moving to Hollywood. His ability to sketch ideas rapidly was the envy of all his colleagues and this talent, combined with Hanna's keen sense of timing and facility with storylines, made them a dynamic duo. Their cat and mouse partnership was equally successful and the first cartoon was nominated for an Oscar. For the next fifteen years, Hanna and Barbera worked on nothing else.

No dialogue is necessary between Tom & Jerry. The situations in their long running cat n' mouse game establish their adversary relationship and lots of hilarious twists alter the balance of

Right: Tom & Jerry cartoon scene

power. Both characters are superbly drawn and animated with a wide range of expressions. Tom harasses his prey with undisguised delight but is suitably deflated when Jerry gets the upper hand with his barrage of practical jokes. Jerry's cocky personality and mischievous grin endeared him to audiences from the very beginning and even the devious Tom demonstrates his softer 'pussy cat' nature on occasion.

In the mid 1940s, the pace of the Tom & Jerry cartoons became much faster and the gags more aggressive, due to the influence of Tex Avery, who had recently arrived at MGM. Avery perfected the gag cartoon with accelerated pacing and outrageous action and the Tom & Jerry stories benefited from these new ingredients. Despite the frenzy of mayhem and slapstick violence, the unstated regard that Tom & Jerry have for each other has contributed to the long term popularity of the cartoon series. The audience realises, whatever happens, that the cat does not actually want to eat the mouse, it is the thrill of the chase that counts.

For Hanna and Barbera, the chase continued until 1957 when MGM decided to close down its animation studio due to the rising costs of cartoon production. Each 6 or 7 minute cartoon took about 6 weeks to produce and cost up to $30,000, money that was not being recouped in box office

Tom & Jerry cartoon scene

Tom, Spike & Jerry cartoon scene

Tom & Jerry

Left: Tom 3552, 1995
Right: Jerry 3547, 1995

receipts. Despite the initial shock, it proved to be a lucky break for Hanna and Barbera as it forced them to open their own highly successful studio producing low cost cartoons for television, notably the Flintstones.

Television created a renaissance of interest in cartoons during the 1960s and MGM decided to create some new Tom & Jerry cinema shorts. Eventually some of these Tom & Jerry cartoons were played on television but there was concern about the violence of their original escapades and, in the mid 1970s, Hanna and Barbera had to recreate their famous characters for the small screen, eliminating any controversial antagonism.

The two figures from the Beswick studio, which were commissioned by UK International Ceramics in 1995, show the pair during a brief truce. Jerry's hand is extended in friendship and Tom smiles down at his little companion — but how long will it be before chaos breaks out again?

TOM & JERRY

John Beswick backstamp

3552	**Tom**	3547	**Jerry**
	Modelled by Simon Ward		Modelled by Simon Ward
	Height: 4½ inches 11.5 cm		Height: 3¼ inches 8 cm
	Introduced: 1995		Introduced: 1995
	Commissioned by		Commissioned by
	UK International Ceramics		UK International Ceramics
	in a limited edition of 2,000		in a limited edition of 2,000

Droopy

I collect Royal Doulton

Right: Droopy cartoon drawing

D ROOPY was the brainchild of Fred 'Tex' Avery, the master of the 'chase' cartoon and the zip-crash school of animation. Avery entered the industry in 1930 and later worked with Walter Lantz on the Oswald the Rabbit cartoons. At Warner Brothers, he directed some of the Merrie Melodies and Looney Tunes and was very influential in the development of their stars, Bugs Bunny and Daffy Duck. After moving to MGM's Animation Studios, he developed his ideas to outlandish extremes and his work during the 1940s was a major influence on the American cartoon industry. His irreverent sense of humour and exaggerated style created hilarious cartoons. He also delighted in visual puns and in overturning conventions by having characters slide off the edge of the film frame and talk direct to camera.

The characters that he created at MGM are essentially vehicles for his outrageous gags, like Droopy the diminutive bloodhound. He made his debut in the 1943 cartoon *Dumb-Hounded* and soon captured the audience's enthusiasm with his deadpan expression and understated comments spoken in a slow nasal drawl. Although he looks exhausted and miserable all the time, he regularly insists 'I'm so happy'. He always gets the better of his over-confident adversaries, Spike the bulldog and the Wolf, both of whom cannot understand how this unassuming underdog can both out-smart and out-run them. Somehow Droopy is always in the right place at the right time. He has a magical ability to move from one spot to the other, even half way across the world, in the blink of an eye.

OPPOSITE PAGE
Droopy 3547, 1995

DROOPY

Droopy starred in 23 feature cartoons from 1943 until 1958, his brilliant career cut short by the closure of the MGM studios in 1957. One of his last cartoons *One Droopy Knight* (1957) was nominated for an Academy Award. Droopy later had a minor but memorable cameo role in the 1988 film *Who Framed Roger Rabbit,* working as an elevator operator in Toon Town.

In 1995, UK International Ceramics commissioned the John Beswick studio to produce a portrait of this famous cartoon canine and Droopy's famous world-weary expression has been captured superbly by modeller Simon Ward in this collectable ceramic figure.

Above: Droopy with flowers

Left: Droopy 3547, 1995

DROOPY

John Beswick backstamp

3547 **Droopy**
Modelled by Simon Ward
Height: 4¼ inches 10.5 cm
Introduced: 1995
Commissioned by
UK International Ceramics
in a limited edition of 2,000

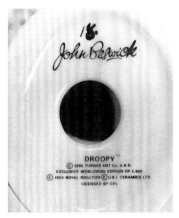

The Flintstones

*Dino 3590,
1996*

THE FLINTSTONES made history in 1960 by being the first animated situation comedy on night-time television and this 'modern stone-age family' is equally popular today with adults and children alike. The series was the brain-wave of William Hanna and Joseph Barbera, who created Tom & Jerry at the MGM studios. When MGM closed their animation department in 1957, Hanna and Barbera formed their own company to make cartoons for television. They developed a more economical system of limited animation, which cost about a tenth of the price of a theatrical cartoon, and they compensated for the lack of detailed movement with excellent comedy scripts and well chosen character voices.

In creating the Flintstones, Hanna and Barbera were inspired by the hugely popular TV series *The Honeymooners* and they envisaged a typical suburban family with all the mod cons but with a prehistoric twist. The Flintstones and their neighbours, the Rubbles, live in the town of Bedrock and use ingenious stone-age gadgetry, such as a woolly mammoth vacuum cleaner that sucks up dirt through its trunk and a ravenous buzzard kept in a cage under the sink for waste disposal!

Everyone can relate to the Flintstones and the Rubbles who enjoy all the usual family activities. In fact life would be pretty predictable if it were not for Fred Flintstone's hair-brain schemes for everything from making money to sneaking out to the bowling alley. His ploys rarely succeed as his long-suffering wife Wilma is never fooled. Fred works as a dinosaur operator at the local gravel pit but passes himself off as everything from a song writer to a sportsman. Even the most innocent situation turns into a fiasco when Fred is involved but his natural exuberance carries him through and is best expressed by his favourite phrase 'Yabba-dabba-doo!'

Wilma is the stabilising influence in the Flintstones family and is a model wife and mother to baby Pebbles. She's helped Fred out of many tricky situations over the years and has the continuing support of her great friend and neighbour Betty Rubble, wife of Barney. Genial but none too bright, Barney is often reluctantly sucked into Fred's follies but he deals with his friend's excesses with good humour and is always quick to forgive. His even temper endears him to family and friends and he is a great husband and father to Bamm-Bamm, the world's strongest kid. He and Pebbles have great fun playing with Dino, the Flintstones' lovable pet dinosaur, who greets Fred nightly with great enthusiasm, knocking him over and slobbering all over his face.

Audiences immediately identified with this light hearted look at human foibles and appreciated all the witty stone-age gags. Not surprisingly the Flintstones became the longest running animated sitcom on prime-time TV and the prehistoric superstars went on to feature in spin-off shows and a variety of feature length movies. Now they have also inspired a series of collectable figures, commissioned by UK International Ceramics from the John Beswick studio in 1995.

Flintstones cartoon scenes

THE FLINTSTONES

The Flintstones

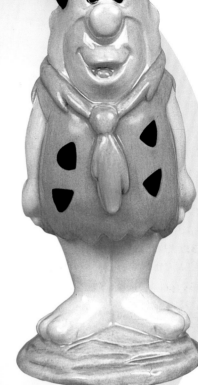

Pebbles 3577, 1996

Bamm-Bamm 3579, 1996

Above left: Wilma Flintstone 3583, 1996

Above right: Fred Flintstone 3588, 1996

Bottom left: Betty Rubble 3584, 1996

Bottom centre: Barney Rubble 3587, 1996

Dino 3590, 1996

The Flintstones

THE FLINTSTONES

John Beswick backstamp

3577 **Pebbles**
Modelled by Simon Ward
Height: 3½ inches 8.5 cm
Introduced: 1996
Commissioned by
UK International Ceramics
in a limited edition of 2,000

3579 **Bamm-Bamm**
Modelled by Simon Ward
Height: 3 inches 7.5 cm
Introduced: 1996
Commissioned by
UK International Ceramics
in a limited edition of 2,000

3583 **Wilma Flintstone**
Modelled by Simon Ward
Height: 4¾ inches 12 cm
Introduced: 1996
Commissioned by
UK International Ceramics
in a limited edition of 2,000

3584 **Betty Rubble**
Modelled by Simon Ward
Height: 4 inches 10 cm
Introduced: 1996
Commissioned by
UK International Ceramics
in a limited edition of 2,000

3587 **Barney Rubble**
Modelled by Simon Ward
Height: 3½ inches 8.5 cm
Introduced: 1996
Commissioned by
UK International Ceramics
in a limited edition of 2,000

3588 **Fred Flintstone**
Modelled by Simon Ward
Height: 4¾ inches 12 cm
Introduced: 1996
Commissioned by
UK International Ceramics
in a limited edition of 2,000

3590 **Dino**
Modelled by Simon Ward
Height: 4¾ inches 12 cm
Introduced: 1996
Commissioned by
UK International Ceramics
in a limited edition of 2,000

Top Cat

Right: Top Cat 3581, 1996

ANOTHER Hanna Barbera creation, Top Cat made his debut on American TV in 1961 and quickly became a firm favourite with audiences around the world, appearing in 28 half hour cartoons. This smart-aleck cat lives with his feline gang in an alley in New York's 13th precinct. Living off their wits, they make their homes in trash cans but constantly try to improve their standard of living through various scams. Their arrangements are made from a police call box and they are always scheming to avoid Officer Dibble, the cop on the beat.

Top Cat was inspired by Sergeant Bilko in Phil Silvers' popular comedy show. Bilko was a fast thinking con-man making creative use of minimal resources; even his name derives from the verb bilk meaning to cheat or defraud. Top Cat shares his character traits but, although he is devious and underhand, it is impossible to dislike this good-natured alley cat.

T.C. as he is known, is always delegating jobs to his friends Choo-Choo, Spook, the Brain, Fancy Fancy and his chief aide Benny the Ball, but they frequently fail him and he ends up blowing the job himself. Invariably the cats always end up back in their alley, no better off for their efforts.

The street-wise, sharp tongued Top Cat generated a more sophisticated type of humour than the average cartoon programme. He was also better drawn than many TV characters

Today's Lesson cartoon scene

and the Beswick studio modellers have produced an excellent likeness with his dapper waistcoat and boater hat. Top Cat was launched at the Doulton and Beswick Collectors Fair in March 1996, together with Choo-Choo, his eager errand runner. The rest of the gang have also been commissioned exclusively for sale at Doulton Fairs in the UK. Look out for the long suffering Officer Dibble; Fancy Fancy, the ladies man; Spook, the genial but foolish hip cat; Benny the Ball, T.C.'s right hand man and Brain, whose minuscule thinking capacity belies his name.

Left: Top Cat cartoon scene

All the repeats of Top Cat's exploits on children's TV, have ensured he is a familiar figure with several generations and the new Beswick portraits are sure to be in great demand with cartoon fans around the world.

Top Cat with Officer Dibble cartoon scene

140

Top Cat

Above: Benny 3627, 1997

Right: Officer Dibble 3671, 1998

Below left: Fancy Fancy 3624, 1997

Below centre: Spook 3673, 1998

Below right: Brain 3674, 1998

Above left: Choo Choo 3586, 1996   *Above right: Top Cat 3581, 1996*

TOP CAT

John Beswick backstamp

3581   **Top Cat**
Modelled by Andy Moss
Height: 4½ inches 11.5 cm
Introduced: 1996
Commissioned for Doulton Fairs in
the UK in a limited edition of 2,000

3586   **Choo-Choo**
Modelled by Andy Moss
Height: 4½ inches 11.5 cm
Introduced: 1996
Commissioned for Doulton Fairs in
the UK in a limited edition of 2,000

3624   **Fancy Fancy**
Modelled by Andy Moss
Height: 4½ inches 11.5 cm
Introduced: 1997
Commissioned for Doulton Fairs in
the UK in a limited edition of 2,000

3627   **Benny**
Modelled by Andy Moss
Height: 3½ inches 8.5 cm
Introduced: 1997
Commissioned for Doulton Fairs in
the UK in a limited edition of 2,000

3671   **Officer Dibble**
Modelled by Andy Moss
Height: 7 inches 17.5 cm
Introduced: 1998
Commissioned for Doulton Fairs in
the UK in a limited edition of 2,000

3673   **Spook**
Modelled by Andy Moss
Height: 4½ inches 11.5 cm
Introduced: 1998
Commissioned for Doulton Fairs in
the UK in a limited edition of 2,000

3674   **Brain**
Modelled by Andy Moss
Height: 4 inches 10 cm
Introduced: 1998
Commissioned for Doulton Fairs in
the UK in a limited edition of 2,000

Paddington Bear

Michael Bond

PADDINGTON is a very rare bear indeed and chaotic things just seem to happen to him. When the Brown family first met him at Paddington Railway Station, he had travelled all the way from darkest Peru as a stowaway, with only a jar of marmalade to eat. He is very attached to his large floppy hat, which he has had since he was small, and the Browns bought him a smart blue duffle coat which he often wears on his adventures.

This engaging children's character first appeared in *A Bear Called Paddington* written by Michael Bond in 1958 and his exploits continued in eleven more stories published between 1959 and 1974. He has featured subsequently in picture books for younger children and on television. Michael Bond was once a television cameraman for the BBC but he devoted himself full time to writing in 1966. He created lots of other stories about animal characters, such as Thursday the orphan mouse, Olga da Polga the guinea pig and Parsley the Lion, but they have not had the same outstanding success as Paddington Bear.

Children respond to Paddington's naive, yet crushing logic as he tries to extricate himself from all the disasters that he brings upon himself. Indeed it is hard not to love this accident prone bear who is so full of good intentions.

The lively line drawings by Peggy Fortnum add an extra dimension to Paddington's character. She trained at the Central School of Arts and Crafts on a war grant and began illustrating children's books in the late 1940s, producing some seventy titles before retiring in 1975. Her light-hearted pen and ink illustrations for the Paddington books are amongst her best work.

Paddington the Golfer PB7, 1996

Paddington Bear™

Apparently the original Paddington was a very tiny bear which Michael Bond found in a London store one Christmas. The toy had been left on the shelf all by himself and the author took pity on him, buying him as a present for his wife. As they lived near Paddington Station at the time, the little bear acquired this distinguished sounding name.

Michael Bond's Paddington character has also had considerable success as a toy bear, dressed in his distinctive hat, duffle coat and bright red wellington boots. He wears a label around his neck, as in the original story, which reads 'Please look after this bear, thank you'. Lots of other character merchandise has followed over the years and now he appears in a collection of Royal Doulton figures.

The twelve Paddington figures were modelled by Valerie Annand in Doulton's resin body which allows the artist to add lots of minute detail. She shows Paddington in many humorous situations as he tries his hand at golfing (PB7), surfing (PB4) and gardening (PB5). Typically he ends up in a muddle, as in PB2 where he bakes a cake and covers himself in icing or in PB3 where he decorates the house with one foot in the bucket of paste and his arm caught in the wallpaper!

Paddington with Suitcase illustration

Paddington with Label illustration

144

Paddington Bear

Above left: Paddington Decorating PB3, 1996-C

Above right: Paddington Bathtime PB6, 1996-C

Below left: Paddington Bakes a Cake PB2, 1996-C

Below: Paddington the Musician PB8, 1996-C

Above: Paddington at the Station PB1, 1996-C

Above: Paddington Gardening PB5, 1996-C

Top left: Paddington the Fisherman PB12, 1997-C

Below left: Paddington at Christmas Time PB9, 1996-C

Below right: Paddington the Golfer PB7, 1996-C

Paddington Bear

Above: Paddington Surfing PB4, 1996-C

Left: Marmalade Sandwiches PB10, 1997-C

Below: Going to bed PB11, 1997-C

PADDINGTON BEAR

Resin figures
Royal Doulton backstamp

PB1 **Paddington at the Station**
Modelled by Valerie Annand
Height: 4¼ inches 10.5 cm
Introduced: 1996   Still in production

PB2 **Paddington Bakes a Cake**
Modelled by Valerie Annand
Height: 4¼ inches 10.5 cm
Introduced: 1996   Still in production

PB3 **Paddington Decorating**
Modelled by Valerie Annand
Height: 4¾ inches 12 cm
Introduced: 1996   Still in production

PB4 **Paddington Surfing**
Modelled by Valerie Annand
Height: 4 inches 10 cm
Introduced: 1996   Still in production

PB5 **Paddington Gardening**
Modelled by Valerie Annand
Height: 4 inches 10 cm
Introduced: 1996   Still in production

PB6 **Paddington Bathtime**
Modelled by Valerie Annand
Height: 3½ inches 8.5 cm
Introduced: 1996   Still in production

PB7 **Paddington the Golfer**
Modelled by Valerie Annand
Height: 3¾ inches 9.5 cm
Introduced: 1996   Still in production

PB8 **Paddington the Musician**
Modelled by Valerie Annand
Height: 3¾ inches 9.5 cm
Introduced: 1996   Still in production

PB9 **Paddington at Christmas Time**
Modelled by Valerie Annand
Height: 3½ inches 8.5 cm
Introduced: 1996   Still in production

PB10 **Marmalade Sandwiches**
Modelled by Valerie Annand
Height: 3½ inches 8.5 cm
Introduced: 1997   Still in production

PB11 **Going to Bed**
Modelled by Valerie Annand
Height: 3¾ inches 9 cm
Introduced: 1997   Still in production

PB12 **Paddington the Fisherman**
Modelled by Valerie Annand
Height: 3½ inches 8.5 cm
Introduced: 1997   Still in production

Noddy and Big Ears

Enid Blyton

Right: Noddy illustration

OPPOSITE PAGE

*Noddy and Big Ears
illustration*

NODDY AND BIG EARS have been part of nursery life since 1949 when Enid Blyton introduced these lovable characters in *Little Noddy Goes to Toyland.* Already a very successful children's author, Miss Blyton (1897-1968) was inspired to create Noddy after seeing the work of a Dutch artist, Harmsen Van Der Beek. In the words of the publisher, his drawings were populated by 'fantastically lively little people, beside tiny houses in the lee of bluebells as proportionately big as trees'. Miss Blyton wrote the Noddy stories around his particular talent for portraying a Toyland inhabited by teddies, golliwogs, pixies and goblins, living happily together in toadstools and doll's houses.

The sales of the first Noddy books exceeded all expectations and Miss Blyton was soon collaborating with Van Der Beek to produce a daily newspaper strip in the London *Evening Standard.* When Van Der Beek died in 1953, other artists took over the drawings, using a pictorial dictionary so that the details were always consistent. Lots of commercial spin-offs followed and Noddy featured on products as diverse as cereal packets, toothbrushes, curtain material and children's china.

The little wooden fellow with the nodding head entered the world of children's literature when he escaped from his maker, the Old Carver, and met Big Ears the Brownie, a genial father figure. Big Ears named his new found friend Noddy and helped him get settled in Toyland. Together they bought some new clothes, including the famous blue hat with a bell on the tip that jingles whenever he speaks and nods his head.

Noddy has been described as a children's Charlie Chaplin, always getting into scrapes and evoking sympathy from his young audience. He combines the naivety and innocence of childhood with the excitement of the adult world by building his own house, working for a living and driving a car.

Although the Noddy books have sold over 100 million copies in a wide range of languages, the character has not been without its critics. During the 1960s, many libraries began to exclude Noddy and other Enid Blyton titles on the grounds that they were racist, sexist and full of stereotyped characters, undemanding plots and repetitive vocabulary. Miss Blyton claimed she paid little attention to any critic over the age of twelve and the Noddy books continued to be purchased for the intended audience.

Many pre-school readers remained faithful to the books throughout childhood, graduating to the *Secret Seven* and *Famous Five* stories and then on to the Circus series and the tales of boarding school life at *St Clare's* and *Malory Towers*.

With over 700 titles to her name, Miss Blyton was one of the world's most prolific children's authors. She could type 10,000 words at one sitting and claimed she could write a whole book in a day if she did not have to eat or sleep. She combined this extraordinary writing ability with outstanding business acumen and all her best-sellers made her a very wealthy woman. Her books are still read widely today and Noddy has been re-established as a pre-school classic, mainly thanks to the BBC TV series launched in 1992. Today Noddy appears in his own magazine, published by the BBC, and there are over 300 licensed products in the UK alone including the Royal Doulton figures of *Noddy* and *Big Ears,* introduced in 1997.

Big Ears, Tessie Bear and Mr Plod illustrations

Noddy and Big Ears

Above: Tessie Bear 3770, 1998

Below: Mr Plod 3769, 1998

Noddy, 3678 and Big Ears, 3676, 1997

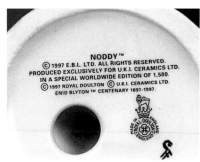

NODDY AND BIG EARS

Royal Doulton backstamp

3676   Big Ears
Modelled by Andy Moss
Height: 5¼ inches 13 cm
Introduced: 1997   Still current
Commissioned by
UK International Ceramics
in a limited edition of 1,500

3678   Noddy
Modelled by Andy Moss
Height: 5 inches 12.5 cm
Introduced: 1997   Still current
Commissioned by
UK International Ceramics
in a limited edition of 1,500

3769   Mr Plod
Modelled by Andy Moss
Introduced in 1998
Commissioned by
UK International Ceramics
in a limited edition of 1,500

3770   Tessie Bear
Modelled by Andy Moss
Introduced in 1998
Commissioned by
UK International Ceramics
in a limited edition of 1,500

The Wizard of Oz

OPPOSITE PAGE
Scarecrow 3709, 1998

W E'RE OFF to see the Wizard, the wonderful Wizard of Oz' sings Judy Garland in MGM's famous musical version of this classic fairy tale. Miss Garland won an oscar for her performance as little Dorothy Gale from Kansas and her emotional rendition of 'Over the Rainbow' melted the hearts of audiences everywhere and became her theme tune.

Although generations of children have been captivated by the 1939 movie, few have read the original story which was written in 1900 by Lynam Frank Baum (1856-1919). In the book, Dorothy's adventures begin when a tornado hits her family's farm in Kansas. Dorothy and her dog, Toto, are trapped inside the house which is blown away to the Land of Oz. It lands on top of the Wicked Witch of the East, who had been terrorising the local community of Munchkins, and Dorothy is proclaimed a heroine. A good witch provides her with a magic pair of silver shoes and advises her to go and see the Wizard of Oz who will help her return home.

Below: Advertising poster for the film

As Dorothy makes her way along the Yellow Brick Road, she meets some very strange characters, including the Scarecrow, Tin Woodman and Cowardly Lion and they travel together to meet the Wizard, believing he will help them all to find what they most want in life. After some hair-raising adventures, they arrive at the Emerald City but discover the Wizard will only grant their wishes once they have killed the Wicked Witch of the East. They achieve this by accident and return to the Wizard who deals with the Cowardly Lion's ambition to be courageous, the Scarecrow's desire for a brain and the Tin Woodman's wish for a heart. However, he is exposed as a fraud and is unable to help Dorothy find her way home. Disappointed, they seek the help of the Good Witch of the South who shows Dorothy that she has the ability to fulfil her dreams within herself, as did her unlikely friends. The story ends happily with Dorothy and Toto returning to Kansas.

Frank Baum wrote many sequels to his best-selling *Wizard of Oz* and he adapted the story for a musical stage production which was a Broadway hit in 1902. By 1914, he had formed the Oz Film Manufacturing Company and made a number of films based on the Oz books but they were not a commercial success and the company was sold. Although Baum was one of the best loved children's writers of the period, he struggled financially throughout his career. In the early days, he supported his writing with a job as a travelling salesman for a china company and one of the lands he created in the Wizard of Oz is made entirely of china, including all the tiny citizens. No doubt he would have been pleased to see his famous characters re-created in this medium by Royal Doulton.

The figures, commissioned by UK International Ceramics, represent *Dorothy*, the *Scarecrow*, the *Tin Woodman* and the *Cowardly Lion* just as they appear in the 1939 MGM film. Modeller, Andy Moss has captured the characters and costumes to perfection. Wide-eyed Dorothy looks pretty as a picture in her pinafore dress and her anthropomorphic friends look suitably bizarre, appealing to Oz fans everywhere.

Over the years Oz fans have been very influential and they persuaded Baum's publishers to continue the stories long after the author's death in 1919. A young children's writer, Ruth Plumly

Above and left: Scenes from the Wizard of Oz film

Thompson, was commissioned to produce annual Oz books which she did with considerable success until 1939. Other writers followed after the war and the International Wizard of Oz club sponsored several new stories in the 1970s and 80s.

The Oz Club was started in 1957 by a Brooklyn teenager, Justin Schiller, and it has grown from 16 founder members to a worldwide membership of several thousand. They publish the Baum Bugle, a

The Wizard of Oz

journal of Oz, and they provide details of all the books and films inspired by Baum's original fantasy. There have been many unusual 'returns' to Oz including an Australian rock version and the all-black stage musical called 'The Wiz' but none have enjoyed the enduring success of the MGM classic. No doubt the Royal Doulton limited edition Oz collection will also become a classic in its own right.

(above and above right) Several variations of the original blond wig were also attempted on October 26.

(left) On October 31, Garland returned to test her own hair once again, with the addition of a long fall in different arrangements.

Above: Judy Garland hairstyles for the film

Left: Wizard of Oz promotional material

The Wizard of Oz

Above left: Scarecrow 3709, 1998

Above centre: Tinman 3738, 1998

Above right: Lion 3731, 1998

Right: Dorothy 3732, 1998

WIZARD OF OZ

Royal Doulton backstamp

3709 **Scarecrow**
Modelled by Andy Moss
Height: 6½ inches 16.5 cm
Introduced: 1998
Commissioned by UK International
Ceramics in a limited edition of 1,500

3731 **Lion**
Modelled by Andy Moss
Height: 6 inches 15 cm
Introduced: 1998
Commissioned by UK International
Ceramics in a limited edition of 1,500

3732 **Dorothy**
Modelled by Andy Moss
Height: 5 inches 12.5 cm
Introduced: 1998
Commissioned by UK International
Ceramics in a limited edition of 1,500

3738 **Tinman**
Modelled by Andy Moss
Height: 7 inches 17.5 cm
Introduced: 1998
Commissioned by UK International
Ceramics in a limited edition of 1,500

Designers and Modellers

OVER THE years a number of very talented artists have contributed to the success of the character figure range, each adding distinctive qualities. In most cases the ideas are developed on paper by one artist and then modelled by another although many of the graphic designers are equally talented as modellers. The majority of artists associated with the cartoon characters have been resident at the John Beswick Studio of Royal Doulton where all the new introductions are made. Details of the artists involved are given below in alphabetical order together with the dates of their careers with Royal Doulton.

Jan Granoska 1951 – 1954

Miss Granoska came from Eastern Europe and trained as a modeller at the Beswick studio under Arthur Gredington. She produced a number of popular character figures in national costume, some dancing and others holding farm animals. She also modelled animals in human situations, notably the *Monkey Band*. In 1952, her portrait of *Mickey Mouse* launched a wonderful collection of *Walt Disney* figures which are all very sought after today.

Arthur Gredington 1939 – 1968

After graduating from the Royal College of Art in London, Arthur Gredington became the first resident modeller at the Beswick factory in 1939. Initially, he specialised in modelling animals, notably famous racehorses, and his skilled work established Beswick as the foremost factory in this field. In 1947, he was responsible for the first *Beatrix Potter* figures and their success led to other collections inspired by famous children's characters such as *David Hand's Animaland* and *Snow White and the Seven Dwarfs*. Gredington retired in 1968 and died three years later.

Albert Hallam 1926 – 1975

Having joined the Beswick factory as an apprentice mould-maker at the age of 14, Albert Hallam became head mould-maker and then graduated to modelling. Initially he produced vases and bowls but by the late 1960s he was working on animal studies. He continued Gredington's work for the *Beatrix Potter* range and he produced several figures for the *Joan Walsh Anglund, Winnie the Pooh* and *Alice in Wonderland* collections.

Miss Joachim 1940

The only works recorded by this freelance modeller are the Beswick plaques inspired by *Cinderella* and *Alice in Wonderland*. There is some doubt whether they ever went into production as examples have not been found.

David Lyttleton 1973 – 1986

Having worked as an electrician, David Lyttleton joined the Beswick studio and studied for a technician's diploma. He produced models to Harry Sales' designs and his work included some of the *Kitty McBride, Alice in Wonderland* and *Snowman* figures and all of the *Tolkien* and *Thelwell* collections. He left the company in 1986.

Charles Noke 1889 – 1941

As Art Director for Royal Doulton from 1913 until his retirement, Charles Noke was responsible for the development of many popular collectables, including series ware, figures, character jugs, and animal studies. He particularly enjoyed modelling animals with human characteristics, such as *Granny Owl* and *Huntsman Fox,* and he adapted the work of many famous illustrators for the Series ware collection, notably Gibson, Souter and Aldin.

Peter Roberts 1966 – 1996

After a varied career in the ceramics industry, Peter Roberts became a designer for the Royal Doulton group and worked on a number of tableware designs for the Royal Albert brand. He was responsible for the development of many nursery and gift ware ranges, including the *World of Beatrix Potter, Brambly Hedge* and *The Snowman*. Peter was appointed Design Director in 1989 and retired in 1996.

Harry Sales 1961 – 1986

Primarily a graphic artist, Harry Sales joined the John Beswick factory in 1960 and was appointed Design Manager in 1975. In that capacity, he was responsible for the development of all products made at the Beswick factory but he became particularly enthusiastic about cartoon classics and other character figures. He designed the *Joan Walsh Anglund, Winnie the Pooh, Alice in Wonderland, Tolkien* and *Rupert Bear* collections. Harry left Royal Doulton in 1986 to pursue a freelance career.

Designers and Modellers

THE PRESENT TEAM

Martyn C R Alcock 1986 – present

Martyn Alcock studied at the North Staffordshire Polytechnic whilst training as a modeller under Graham Tongue at the Beswick studio. He has a talent for modelling character animals and has done a lot of work for the *Bunnykins* and *Beatrix Potter* figure collections. He has also contributed to the *Brambly Hedge, Winnie the Pooh* (second series) and the *101 Dalmatians* collections.

Valerie Annand 1989 – present

Valerie worked for 15 years as a designer of greetings cards at Valentine's of Dundee before embarking on a free-lance career. She had no formal training in modelling but Royal Doulton's Design Director was very impressed with her portfolio and commissioned her first figure sculpture in 1989. Since then, she had made a major contribution to the HN collection and is well known for her fashionable ladies in Victorian and Edwardian dress. Although portraying cute teddies was part of her graphic career, modelling the escapades of Paddington Bear in resin was a new departure for her.

Bill Harper 1971 – present

A graduate of painting and pottery from the Burslem School of Art, Bill Harper taught art until he joined the ceramic industry at the age of 29. He worked for Wade and W H Bossons before becoming a freelance modeller for Royal Doulton. He has designed more than 400 figures and character jugs for the company, including the *Alice in Wonderland* jug collection. He was also responsible for the set of *Thunderbirds* busts.

Amanda Hughes-Lubeck 1988 – present

A graduate of the Sir Henry Doulton School of Sculpture, Amanda is a versatile artist. She particularly enjoys modelling animals, whether they be naturalistic or anthropomorphic. She has contributed a number of models to the *Bunnykins* and *Beatrix Potter* collections and she has also worked on the second *Snow White* series.

Alan Maslankowski 1967 – present

At the age of 15, Alan Maslankowski joined the Royal Doulton group as an apprentice modeller and the company arranged for him to attend classes at the Burslem School of Art. His training complete, he began producing animal models for the Beswick range. In 1988 he modelled a couple of figures for the *Wind in the Willows* collection. He is now a resident modeller for Royal Doulton, specialising in figures for the HN collection.

Andy Moss 1995 – present

When Andy Moss left school, his potential as a ceramic modeller was recognised by Peggy Davies, the celebrated Royal Doulton designer. She trained him in her own studio and, when she died, her husband gave Andy all her modelling tools. Since the late 1980s, Andy has produced many tobies and character jugs for the Peggy Davies studios, including a portrait of the author, Louise Irvine. He also works on a freelance basis for other companies and he was commissioned to model the figures for the *Top Cat*, *Noddy* and *Wizard of Oz* collections in 1995 and 1997.

Pauline Parsons 1977 – present

A sculpture graduate of Manchester School of Art, Pauline Parsons began working as a freelance figure modeller for Royal Doulton in 1977. She specialises in fair ladies and has produced many limited edition collections, including *The Wives of Henry VIII* and *The Gentle Arts*. She has recently completed *The Princess* collection for Walt Disney, combining the traditional elegance of Royal Doulton's crinoline ladies with the most famous heroines from the world of animation.

Warren Platt 1985 – present

It was a Youth Training Scheme that introduced Warren Platt to the Beswick Studio and he quickly demonstrated his natural abilities as a modeller. He studied at Stafford Art School and became a full-time modeller in 1986. He works primarily on the storybook characters, including the *Beatrix Potter* and *Bunnykins* range. He modelled some of the recent *Winnie the Pooh* and *Snow White* figures and contributed most of the *Snowman* collection.

Shane Ridge 1994 – present

Shane Ridge joined Royal Doulton as a tableware modeller after a varied career in the industry, with experience in mouldmaking and relief modelling. He further honed his skills at Stoke Polytechnic. In 1994 he transferred to the Beswick studio where he has been working on the second *Winnie the Pooh* series, the second *Snow White* series and the *101 Dalmatians* series.

Designers and Modellers

Graham Tongue 1966 – present

An experienced designer and modeller, Graham Tongue joined the John Beswick factory in 1966 becoming Head Modeller in 1973. He specialised in naturalistic animal studies but he also modelled several cartoon characters to Harry Sales designs in the 1970s and 80s, including some of the *Winnie the Pooh* and *Alice in Wonderland* figures and all of the *Rupert Bear* collection. He was appointed Design Manager in 1986, assuming responsibility for the *Snowman* range amongst others. Graham now works from his own studio, producing Royal Doulton commissions.

Simon Ward 1995 – present

Pottery and art were Simon Ward's chief interests at school and he went on to achieve a first class honours degree in ceramics at South Glamorgan Institute. After graduating, he attended cartoon evening classes and taught part time before studying for an MA at the Royal College of Art. He was awarded the RSA award for tableware design which led to his freelance association with Royal Doulton. He now works as a lecturer at Edinburgh College of Art and models cartoon characters for the company in his spare time, notably *Tom & Jerry, Droopy, The Flintstones* and the character jugs from the *Beano* and the *Dandy* comics.

Creating a Cartoon Collectable

From concept to collector's cabinet

IAN HOWE

THE PROCESS of transforming an idea into a ceramic model is a lengthy one. The traditional methods by which Royal Doulton products are made, with their emphasis on hand-skills, and the need to ensure that the product ultimately meets with expectations, mean that it often takes around a year from the initial concept for the first finished piece to reach the collector.

The reasons for choosing a cartoon character in the first place are much the same as those for the selection of any subject for a ceramic model. The marketing department at Royal Doulton has the responsibility to develop new products within all the categories covered by our ranges. As well as independently coming up with subject matter for new products, the Brand Managers within the department will actively seek out suggestions from other sources. Ideas for new products can come from many directions. Collectors often have suggestions for new products or for extensions to an existing range, and these can come to the company via the Royal Doulton International Collectors Club or our Consumer Enquiries team. Retailers and dealers in collectable products frequently put forward ideas, and of course there is also inspiration from the designers and modellers. From all this, the marketing department selects which ideas should be developed, basing their choice on what products it is felt will have the strongest appeal to consumers, and which will consequently yield the highest sales.

Why, then, have Royal Doulton and Beswick so often turned to cartoon characters? The principal reason is that such characters are already well-known, widely recognised and popular even before work has begun on a ceramic image of them. We therefore have the opportunity to create a product for which a market already exists, often in many parts of the world, and to target that product to an established body of collectors. When a cartoon character has a worldwide following, then a Royal Doulton or Beswick product based on that character will appeal to that audience, and also to the collectors of Royal Doulton and Beswick, so increasing the marketability.

Not all cartoon characters are suitable for ceramic collectables, however. Because of the high perceived value of china pieces, the

OPPOSITE PAGE

Andy Moss working on the clay models of two Royal Doulton cartoon figures, Spike & Tyke, and Felix the Cat, which will be produced in 1998 exclusively for UK International Ceramics Ltd.

high cost base created by the hand-skills involved and the considerable lead times, we are not competing with cheap plastic replicas of the latest hot property. To fit in with the medium used, the characters must be classics, with established longevity, not here today gone tomorrow ephemera: Walt Disney rather than Teenage Mutant Ninja Turtles.

The choice of subjects from the D C Thomson comic stable, for example, was based on the long history of the characters involved. Dennis the Menace and Desperate Dan first appeared in the 1930s, since when generations have grown up with their adventures. Many children who laughed at Dennis' antics in their youth have carried their affection for him into adulthood, and can now seriously consider buying high-value collectables such as our character jugs. While these particular characters are a purely British phenomenon, the same is true on a worldwide scale for Walt Disney and Warner Brothers favourites, as demonstrated by the success of the chains of stores operated by those two companies. Like them, we are appealing not to the children for whom the characters were originally created, but to adult collectors who still love them.

The final criterion in the selection of a cartoon character is that it is a suitable subject for the type of piece involved. Character jugs have a long tradition of humour, and even their name shows how suited they are to represent particular characters. In the field of figures, the Walt Disney *Princesses* beautifully combine the grace and elegance of their subjects with that for which Royal Doulton figures are world famous. And the John Beswick studios have a long tradition of creating delightful little figures of popular characters, of which the most familiar are probably those from the tales of Beatrix Potter. The choice of the most suitable brand to feature on the backstamp of the piece is closely associated with the established traditions of the various companies which are now part of Royal Doulton.

There are also some products which do not form part of the standard range of Royal Doulton products generally available, but which are created in response to special commissions from various companies. It was with an eye to the tradition of the Beswick studios that UK International Ceramics came to Royal Doulton wishing to develop figures of *The Flintstones*, for instance. Special commissions are accepted by Royal Doulton subject to certain restrictions, including minimum

'Exploded' mould of limited edition piece. Eight moulds are required to make this piece, and each mould comprises of several parts

Creating a Cartoon Collectable

quantities and distribution considerations, and also to acceptance of the subject matter. Once again, classic status is the key.

Once it has been decided to develop a cartoon character, the first step in every case is to obtain a licence. If a character is well-known, it is certain that someone, somewhere, will own all rights to that character, and if a reproduction of it is to be made, permission must be obtained and a licence signed. The licence agreement will include detailed restrictions and requirements, including the need for approval by the licensor at every stage, and in most cases a royalty will be payable based on a percentage of the price of the piece.

After permission has been obtained and details of the licence finalised, agreement is reached with the licensor on the design of the piece. This is supplied together with detailed reference material to Royal Doulton's Design Department, who decide on the most suitable modeller to create the three-dimensional clay model. The model, which may take several weeks to complete dependent upon size and complexity, must then be approved by the licensor, and it is possible that amendments may be required. Once the model has been approved, it is passed to the blockmaker who creates the master block mould. It is not always appreciated that to do this, the original model must be cut up into pieces which are capable of being taken from a mould. Thus in the creation of replicas the original model is destroyed.

From the first block mould, a small number of models are cast, and, using the reference material supplied, a decorated piece is prepared for approval. Often the colours of a cartoon character are very precisely defined, and it can be difficult to recreate them accurately with ceramic colours. The vivid pink of Fred Flintstone's pet dinosaur, Dino, proved quite a challenge and has come to be known on the factory as 'Dino pink'.

Below left: Filling a mould with slip or liquid clay

Below right: Opening a mould and removing the head

Finally, we have an approved, decorated prototype, and production can begin. From the master block mould, working case moulds are created and it is from these that the production pieces are cast. The precise formulation of the ceramic body used for the piece depends upon the type of model and the factory in which it is produced. At John Beswick, where some of the small figures and all character jugs are made, the body is earthenware, while at the figure factory in Burslem, bone china is used for pretty ladies and fine china for character figures, as each has characteristics particularly suited to the style and decoration of such pieces.

Whatever the body, the first stage of production is much the same. Liquid clay, called slip, is poured into a plaster mould for each individual part of the model. Within a few minutes, water from the slip is absorbed into the plaster, forming a thin layer of clay around the internal surfaces of the mould. After the right length of time, the excess slip is poured out, the mould taken apart and the clay part removed. Each time a mould is used, it loses a little of its detail, and so the use of each mould is carefully controlled, and worn moulds discarded.

The various parts are then assembled, using the same slip from which they were cast to attach one to the other. Any excess slip around the joins is carefully removed in a process called fettling. The piece is left to dry, which may take several days, before it is given its first firing. This biscuit firing, as it is known, varies dependent upon the type of product and body. A bone china figure will be fired at around 1250°C, but an earthenware piece at a slightly lower temperature. In all cases, the piece will shrink by some 12% during the firing as all the moisture held within it evaporates.

The next stage of production depends upon whether the piece is to be decorated underglaze or onglaze. The two techniques offer distinctively different effects. Traditionally pretty ladies are painted onglaze, which gives a smooth, elegant effect suited to their beauty, while character pieces are painted underglaze,

Above: Cartoon characters waiting for their first firing in the biscuit kiln

Top: Assembling Lucky, the head is attached to the body using liquid slip

166

Creating a Cartoon Collectable

which can give a more rugged look, particularly on flesh tones. Some pieces use a combination of the two techniques to achieve specific colour effects. Bright colours in particular can generally be achieved only with onglaze decoration, and consequently many cartoon characters require it to achieve their distinctive colouring.

For onglaze decoration, the biscuit piece is dipped in liquid glaze and fired once more at 1050°C before it is passed on to the decorating department. There, colour is applied onto the glaze, and the piece fired again. Some figures require several applications of colour, and consequently multiple firings, to achieve the final effect. During firing, the colour combines with the glaze to create a permanent, unfading hue with a lustrous finish.

Other pieces are taken for underglaze decoration after the first biscuit fire, and colour is applied directly onto the body. This is left to dry, and may be followed by further applications to create the desired appearance, before the piece is glazed and fired.

All through the process, each piece is subject to inspection and control, to ensure that all meet with the standards required. One of the final touches is the application of the Royal Doulton backstamp, and for limited edition pieces the very last process is the engraving of the unique edition number onto the base.

Right: Painting Perdita

Below left: Pongo waiting to be glazed

Below centre: Glazing Pongo — dipped by hand in a vat of glaze

Below right: Applying the backstamp to Perdita

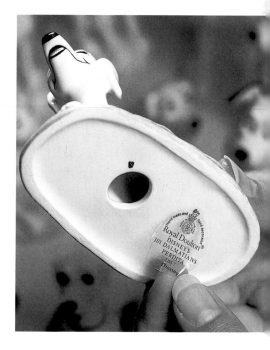

Tours are available at both the Royal Doulton figure factory in Burslem and the John Beswick Studios in Longton, while the former also houses the new Royal Doulton Visitor Centre, the Home of the Royal Doulton Figure. Why not visit Stoke-on-Trent to see for yourself the work that goes into every one of these pieces? For further details contact the tour organisers on 01782 292292.

Cartoon characters recreated by the Royal Doulton company can be seen in many different channels of distribution, from traditional china stores to The Disney Store, in mail order catalogues and at collector's events. Each, it is believed, is particularly suited to that area and the collectors and customers who will see it there. There are many people who already collect either Royal Doulton pieces or cartoon characters. Looking back at the wealth of Royal Doulton pieces which represent cartoon characters of all types, and forward to new developments around the corner, it is clear that an opportunity also exists for the collector exclusively of Royal Doulton's cartoon characters.

View of the decorating department where the cartoon characters, Beatrix Potter and Bunnykins figures are painted

168

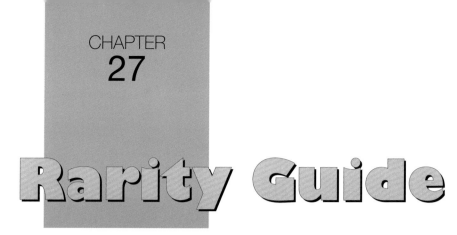

Rarity Guide

NICK TZIMAS

THIS guide has been compiled in response to frequent requests from collectors and is intended to provide an indication of relative scarcity. It must be stressed that the comparative rarity of the cartoon and character figures is a matter of opinion and these assessments are based on my personal experience of the market, particularly in the last five years.

Cartoon figures appear regularly at auction and Beswick dealers carry stocks of discontinued models. Saleroom results and prices at antique shows and markets have been monitored and then related to purchases and collector demand to produce these estimates. Other valuation criteria include: introduction dates; production periods and factory marks.

After much deliberation, figures have been assigned one of six rarity categories. As this is a controversial subject, no doubt some collectors will have different ideas based on the elusiveness of particular models in different parts of the world. The fact that a figure has been designated 'common' need not detract from its desirability. Some of the most appealing subjects fall into this category as they were best selling models with wide aesthetic appeal. In the end rarity is determined by what collectors want and the prices they are prepared to pay, not by dealers and guides.

Note: These rarity categories are for standard figures without colour, model or backstamp variations.

RARITY CATEGORIES

A:	EXTREMELY RARE
B:	VERY RARE
C:	RARE
D:	LESS COMMON
E:	COMMON
F:	STILL IN PRODUCTION

First Series
John Beswick backstamp

857   **Alice and the White Rabbit**
Modelled by Miss Joachim
Introduced: 1940   Withdrawn: 1940
Rarity: A

858   **The Dormouse and Alice Plaque**
Modelled by Miss Joachim
Introduced: 1940   Withdrawn: 1940
Rarity: A

859   **The King and Alice Plaque**
Modelled by Miss Joachim
Introduced: 1940   Withdrawn: 1940
Rarity: A

860   **Alice Playing Croquet**
Modelled by Miss Joachim
Introduced: 1940   Withdrawn: 1940
Rarity: A

Second Series
John Beswick backstamp
Designed by Harry Sales

2476   **Alice**
Modelled by Albert Hallam and
Graham Tongue
Height: 4³/₄ inches 12 cm
Introduced: 1975   Withdrawn: 1981
Rarity: C

2477   **White Rabbit**
Modelled by Graham Tongue
Height: 4³/₄ inches 12 cm
Introduced: 1975   Withdrawn: 1981
Rarity: C

2478   **Mock Turtle**
Modelled by Graham Tongue
Height: 4¹/₄ inches 10.5 cm
Introduced: 1975   Withdrawn: 1981
Rarity: D

2479   **Mad Hatter**
Modelled by Graham Tongue
Height: 4¹/₄ inches 10.5 cm
Introduced: 1975   Withdrawn: 1981
Rarity: C

2480   **Cheshire Cat**
Modelled by Graham Tongue
Height: 1³/₄ inches 4.5 cm
Introduced: 1975   Withdrawn: 1981
Rarity: B

2485   **Gryphon**
Modelled by Albert Hallam
Height: 3¹/₄ inches 8 cm
Introduced: 1975   Withdrawn: 1981
Rarity: D

2489   **King of Hearts**
Modelled by Graham Tongue
Height: 3³/₄ inches 9.5 cm
Introduced: 1975   Withdrawn: 1981
Rarity: D

2490   **Queen of Hearts**
Modelled by Graham Tongue
Height: 4 inches 10 cm
Introduced: 1975   Withdrawn: 1981
Rarity: D

2545   **Dodo**
Modelled by David Lyttleton
Height: 4 inches 10 cm
Introduced: 1976   Withdrawn: 1981
Rarity: C

2546   **Fish Footman**
Modelled by David Lyttleton
Height: 4³/₄ inches 12 cm
Introduced: 1976   Withdrawn: 1981
Rarity: C

2547   **Frog Footman**
Modelled by David Lyttleton
Height: 4¹/₄ inches 10.5 cm
Introduced: 1976   Withdrawn: 1981
Rarity: C

2295   **Display stand**
Height: 2¹/₂ inches 6.5 cm
Introduced: 1977   Withdrawn: 1997
This was also used for other series
and from 1989 to 1997 carried a
Royal Doulton backstamp.
Rarity: E

BONZO AND OOLOO

Royal Doulton backstamp
Designed by George Studdy

Bonzo in five models and various colourways
Introduced: 1922   Withdrawn: 1936

Bonzo lying down
Version 1, model 392
Height: 1 inch 2.5 cm
HN804   cream
          Rarity: A

Bonzo sitting with mouth wide open
Version 2, model 389
Height: 2 inches 5 cm
HN805A purple
HN809   yellow
HN811   blue
          Chinese Jade
          Rarity: A

Rarity Guide

Bonzo sitting with mouth open a little
Version 3, model 387
Height: 2 inches 5 cm
HN805B purple/blue
HN808 cream with black spots
HN810 green
HN812 orange/yellow
Rarity: A

Bonzo wearing a buttoned jacket
Version 4, model 393
Height: 2 inches 5 cm
HN814 black buttons
HN815 red buttons
HN826 red
Rarity: A

Bonzo with head leaning back
Version 5, model 388
Height: 1½ inches 3 cm
No HN numbers recorded
Rarity: A

Ooloo the cat (Lucky)
Model 400 in various colourways
Introduced: 1923 Withdrawn: c1932
HN818 black with white face
Rarity: A
HN819 white
Rarity: A
HN827 ginger
Rarity: A
HN828 tabby
Rarity: A
HN829 black and white
Rarity: A
K12 (1932 – 1975)
black with white face
Rarity: D

BRAMBLY HEDGE

Royal Doulton backstamp
Designed by Harry Sales

DBH1 **Poppy Eyebright**
from *Summer Story*
Modelled by David Lyttleton
Height: 3¼ inches 8 cm
Introduced: 1983   Withdrawn: 1997
Rarity: E

DBH2 **Mr Apple**
from *Winter Story*
Modelled by David Lyttleton
Height: 3¼ inches 8 cm
Introduced: 1983   Withdrawn: 1997
Rarity: E

DBH3 **Mrs Apple**
from *Winter Story*
Modelled by David Lyttleton
Height: 3¼ inches 8 cm
Introduced: 1983   Withdrawn: 1997
Rarity: E

DBH4 **Lord Woodmouse**
from *Autumn Story*
Modelled by David Lyttleton
Height: 3¼ inches 8 cm
Introduced: 1983   Withdrawn: 1997
Rarity: E

DBH5 **Lady Woodmouse**
from *Autumn Story*
Modelled by David Lyttleton
Height: 3¼ inches 8 cm
Introduced: 1983   Withdrawn: 1997
Rarity: E

DBH6 **Dusty Dogwood**
from *Summer Story*
Modelled by David Lyttleton
Height: 3¼ inches 8 cm
Introduced: 1983   Withdrawn: 1997
Rarity: E

DBH7 **Wilfred Toadflax**
from *Spring Story*
Modelled by David Lyttleton
Height: 3¼ inches 8 cm
Introduced: 1983   Withdrawn: 1997
Rarity: E

DBH8 **Primrose Woodmouse**
from *Autumn Story*
Modelled by David Lyttleton
Height: 3¼ inches 8 cm
Introduced: 1983   Withdrawn: 1997
Rarity: E

DBH9 **Old Mrs Eyebright**
from *Summer Story*
Modelled by David Lyttleton
Height: 3¼ inches 8 cm
Introduced: 1984   Withdrawn: 1997
Rarity: E

DBH10 **Mr Toadflax**
from *Spring Story*
Modelled by David Lyttleton
Height: 3¼ inches 8 cm
Introduced: 1984   Withdrawn: 1997
The tail of this figure was remodelled
shortly after its introduction
Rarity: E

DBH11 **Mrs Toadflax**
from *Winter Story*
Modelled by David Lyttleton
Height: 3¼ inches 8 cm
Introduced: 1985   Withdrawn: 1995
Rarity: D

DBH12 Catkin
from *Winter Story*
Modelled by David Lyttleton
Height: 3¼ inches 8 cm
Introduced: 1985   Withdrawn: 1994
Rarity: D

DBH13 Old Vole
from *Summer Story*
Modelled by David Lyttleton
Height: 3¼ inches 8 cm
Introduced: 1985   Withdrawn: 1992
Rarity: C

DBH14 Basil
from *Summer Story*
Modelled by David Lyttleton
Height: 3¼ inches 8 cm
Introduced: 1985   Withdrawn: 1992
Rarity: C

DBH15 Mrs Crustybread
from *Spring Story*
Modelled by Ted Chawner
Height: 3¼ inches 8 cm
Introduced: 1987   Withdrawn: 1994
Rarity: D

DBH16 Clover
from *Winter Story*
Modelled by Graham Tongue
Height: 3¼ inches 8 cm
Introduced: 1987   Withdrawn: 1997
Rarity: E

DBH17 Teasel
from *Winter Story*
Modelled by Ted Chawner
Height: 3¼ inches 8 cm
Introduced: 1987   Withdrawn: 1992
Rarity: C

DBH18 Store Stump Money Box
Modelled by Martyn Alcock
Height: 3¼ inches 8 cm
Introduced: 1987   Withdrawn: 1989
Rarity: C

DBH19 Lily Weaver
from *The High Hills*
Modelled by Ted Chawner
Height: 3¼ inches 8 cm
Introduced: 1988   Withdrawn: 1993
Rarity: C

DBH20 Flax Weaver
from *The High Hills*
Modelled by Ted Chawner
Height: 3¼ inches 8 cm
Introduced: 1988   Withdrawn: 1993
Rarity: C

DBH21 Conker
from *Summer Story*
Modelled by Ted Chawner
Height: 3¼ inches 8 cm
Introduced: 1988   Withdrawn: 1994
Rarity: D

DBH22 Primrose Entertains
from *The Secret Staircase*
Modelled by Alan Maslankowski
Height: 3¼ inches 8 cm
Introduced: 1990   Withdrawn: 1995
Rarity: D

DBH23 Wilfred Entertains
from *The Secret Staircase*
Modelled by Alan Maslankowski
Height: 3¼ inches 8 cm
Introduced: 1990   Withdrawn: 1995
Rarity: E

DBH24 Mr Saltapple
from *The Sea Story*
Modelled by Warren Platt
Height: 2¼ inches 5.5 cm
Introduced: 1993   Withdrawn: 1997
Rarity: E

DBH25 Mrs Saltapple
from *The Sea Story*
Modelled by Warren Platt
Height: 3½ inches 8.5 cm
Introduced: 1993   Withdrawn: 1997
Rarity: E

DBH26 Dusty and Baby
from *Poppy's Babies*
Modelled by Martyn Alcock
Height: 2¾ inches 7 cm
Introduced: 1995   Withdrawn: 1997
Rarity: E

THE DANDY AND THE BEANO

Royal Doulton backstamp

D7005 Dennis and Gnasher
Character jug L/S
Modelled by Simon Ward
Height: 7 inches 17.5 cm
Introduced: 1995   Still in production
Rarity: F

D7006 Desperate Dan
Character jug L/S
Modelled by Simon Ward
Height: 7 inches 17.5 cm
Introduced: 1995   Still in production
Rarity: F

Rarity Guide

D7033 Dennis and Gnasher
Character jug S/S
Modelled by Simon Ward
Height: 4 inches 10 cm
Introduced: 1996   Still in production
Rarity: F

D7034 Desperate Dan
Character jug S/S
Modelled by Simon Ward
Height: 4 inches 10 cm
Introduced: 1996   Still in production
Rarity: F

D7035 Plug
Character jug S/S
Modelled by Simon Ward
Height: 4 inches 10 cm
Introduced: 1996   Still in production
Rarity: F

D7036 Minnie the Minx
Character jug S/S
Modelled by Simon Ward
Height: 4 inches 10 cm
Introduced: 1996   Still in production
Rarity: F

DAVID HAND'S ANIMALAND

John Beswick backstamp

1148 Dinkum Platypus
Modelled by Arthur Gredington
Height: 4^1/$_4$ inches 10.5 cm
Introduced: 1950   Withdrawn: 1955
Rarity: C

1150 Zimmy the Lion
Modelled by Arthur Gredington
Height: 3^3/$_4$ inches 9.5 cm
Introduced: 1950   Withdrawn: 1955
Rarity: B

1151 Felia
Modelled by Arthur Gredington
Height: 4 inches 10 cm
Introduced: 1950   Withdrawn: 1955
Rarity: B

1152 Ginger Nutt
Modelled by Arthur Gredington
Height: 4 inches 10 cm
Introduced: 1950   Withdrawn: 1955
Rarity: C

1153 Hazel Nutt
Modelled by Arthur Gredington
Height: 3^3/$_4$ inches 9.5 cm
Introduced: 1950   Withdrawn: 1955
Rarity: B

1154 Oscar Ostrich
Modelled by Arthur Gredington
Height: 3^3/$_4$ inches 9.5 cm
Introduced: 1950   Withdrawn: 1955
Rarity: B

1155 Dusty Mole
Modelled by Arthur Gredington
Height: 3^1/$_2$ inches 8.5 cm
Introduced: 1950   Withdrawn: 1955
Rarity: C

1156 Loopy Hare
Modelled by Arthur Gredington
Height: 4^1/$_4$ inches 10.5 cm
Introduced: 1950   Withdrawn: 1955
Rarity: B

DROOPY

John Beswick backstamp

3547 Droopy
Modelled by Simon Ward
Height: 4^1/$_4$ inches 10.5 cm
Introduced: 1995
Commissioned by
UK International Ceramics
in a limited edition of 2,000

THE FLINTSTONES

John Beswick backstamp

3577 Pebbles
Modelled by Simon Ward
Height: 3^1/$_2$ inches 8.5 cm
Introduced: 1996
Commissioned by
UK International Ceramics
in a limited edition of 2,000

3579 Bamm-Bamm
Modelled by Simon Ward
Height: 3 inches 7.5 cm
Introduced: 1996
Commissioned by
UK International Ceramics
in a limited edition of 2,000

3583 **Wilma Flintstone**
Modelled by Simon Ward
Height: 4³/₄ inches 12 cm
Introduced: 1996
Commissioned by
UK International Ceramics
in a limited edition of 2,000

3584 **Betty Rubble**
Modelled by Simon Ward
Height: 4 inches 10 cm
Introduced: 1996
Commissioned by
UK International Ceramics
in a limited edition of 2,000

3587 **Barney Rubble**
Modelled by Simon Ward
Height: 3¹/₂ inches 8.5 cm
Introduced: 1996
Commissioned by
UK International Ceramics
in a limited edition of 2,000
Rarity: LE

3588 **Fred Flintstone**
Modelled by Simon Ward
Height: 4³/₄ inches 12 cm
Introduced: 1996
Commissioned by
UK International Ceramics
in a limited edition of 2,000

3590 **Dino**
Modelled by Simon Ward
Height: 4³/₄ inches 12 cm
Introduced: 1996
Commissioned by
UK International Ceramics
in a limited edition of 2,000

M I HUMMEL

John Beswick backstamp

903 **Bugle Boy**
Hummel 97
Modelled by Arthur Gredington
Height: 4¹/₂ inches 11.5 cm
Introduced: 1940   Withdrawn: 1948
Rarity: B

904 **Book Worm**
Hummel 3
Modelled by Arthur Gredington
Height: 5 inches 12.5 cm
Introduced: 1940   Withdrawn: 1948
Rarity: B

905 **Goose Girl**
Hummel 47
Modelled by Arthur Gredington
Height: 6¹/₄ inches 16 cm
Introduced: 1940   Withdrawn: 1948
Rarity: B

906 **Strolling Along**
Hummel 5
Modelled by Arthur Gredington
Height: 4³/₄ inches 12 cm
Introduced: 1941   Withdrawn: 1948
Rarity: B

908 **Stormy Weather**
Hummel 71
Modelled by Arthur Gredington
Height: 6 inches 15 cm
Introduced: 1941   Withdrawn: 1948
Rarity: B

909 **Puppy Love**
Hummel 1
Modelled by Arthur Gredington
Height: 5¹/₄ inches 13 cm
Introduced: 1941   Withdrawn: 1948
Rarity: B

910 **Meditation**
Hummel 13
Modelled by Arthur Gredington
Height: 5 inches 12.5 cm
Introduced: 1941   Withdrawn: 1948
Rarity: B

911 **Max and Moritz**
Hummel 123
Modelled by Arthur Gredington
Height: 5³/₄ inches 14.5 cm
Introduced: 1941   Withdrawn: 1948
Rarity: B

912 **Farm Boy**
Hummel 66
Modelled by Arthur Gredington
Height: 6 inches 15 cm
Introduced: 1941   Withdrawn: 1948
Rarity: B

913 **Globe Trotter**
Hummel 109
Modelled by Arthur Gredington
Height: 5 inches 12.5 cm
Introduced: 1941   Withdrawn: 1948
Rarity: B

914 **Shepherd Boy**
Hummel 64
Modelled by Arthur Gredington
Height: 4³/₄ inches 12 cm
Introduced: 1941   Withdrawn: 1948
Rarity: B

990 **Happiness**
Hummel 86
Modelled by Arthur Gredington
Height: 3 inches 7.5 cm
Prototype model 1942
Not put into production
Rarity: A

Rarity Guide

JOAN WALSH ANGLUND

John Beswick backstamp

Designed by Harry Sales

2272   Anglund Boy
Modelled by Albert Hallam
Height: 4¹/₂ inches 12 cm
Introduced: 1970   Withdrawn: 1971
Rarity: C

2293   Anglund Girl with Doll
Modelled by Albert Hallam
Height: 4¹/₂ inches 12 cm
Introduced: 1970   Withdrawn: 1971
Rarity: C

2317   Anglund Flower Girl
Modelled by Albert Hallam
Height: 4³/₄ inches 12 cm
Introduced: 1971   Withdrawn: 1971
Rarity: C

KITTY MACBRIDE

John Beswick backstamp

2526   A Family Mouse
Modelled by Graham Tongue
Height: 3¹/₂ inches 8.5 cm
Introduced: 1976   Withdrawn: 1982
Rarity: D

2527   A Double Act
Modelled by Graham Tongue
Height: 3¹/₂ inches 8.5 cm
Introduced: 1976   Withdrawn: 1982
Rarity: D

2528   The Racegoer
Modelled by David Lyttleton
Height: 3¹/₂ inches 8.5 cm
Introduced: 1976   Withdrawn: 1982
Rarity: D

2529   A Good Read
Modelled by David Lyttleton
Height: 3¹/₂ inches 8.5 cm
Introduced: 1976   Withdrawn: 1982
Rarity: C

2530   Lazybones
Modelled by David Lyttleton
Height: 1¹/₂ inches 4 cm
Introduced: 1976   Withdrawn: 1982
Rarity: D

2531   A Snack
Modelled by David Lyttleton
Height: 3¹/₄ inches 8 cm
Introduced: 1976   Withdrawn: 1982
Rarity: D

2532   Strained Relations
Modelled by David Lyttleton
Height: 3 inches 7.5 cm
Introduced: 1976   Withdrawn: 1982
Rarity: D

2533   Just Good Friends
Modelled by David Lyttleton
Height: 3 inches 7.5 cm
Introduced: 1976   Withdrawn: 1982
Rarity: D

2565   The Ring
Modelled by David Lyttleton
Height: 3¹/₄ inches 8 cm
Introduced: 1976   Withdrawn: 1983
Rarity: D

2566   Guilty Sweethearts
Modelled by David Lyttleton
Height: 2¹/₄ inches 5.5 cm
Introduced: 1976   Withdrawn: 1983
Rarity: D

2589   All I Do is Think of You
Modelled by David Lyttleton
Height: 2¹/₂ inches 6.5 cm
Introduced: 1977   Withdrawn: 1983
Rarity: C

THE LORD OF THE RINGS

Royal Doulton backstamp

Designed by Harry Sales

HN2911 Gandalf
Modelled by David Lyttleton
Height: 7 inches 17.5 cm
Introduced: 1980   Withdrawn: 1984
Rarity: D

HN2912 Frodo
Modelled by David Lyttleton
Height: 4¹/₂ inches 11.5 cm
Introduced: 1980   Withdrawn: 1984
Rarity: D

HN2913 Gollum
Modelled by David Lyttleton
Height: 3¹/₄ inches 8 cm
Introduced: 1980   Withdrawn: 1984
Rarity: D

HN2914 Bilbo
Modelled by David Lyttleton
Height: 4¹/₄ inches 10.5 cm
Introduced: 1980   Withdrawn: 1984
Rarity: D

HN2915 Galadriel
Modelled by David Lyttleton
Height: 5$\frac{1}{2}$ inches 13.5 cm
Introduced: 1981   Withdrawn: 1984
Rarity: D

HN2916 Aragorn
Modelled by David Lyttleton
Height: 6 inches 15 cm
Introduced: 1981   Withdrawn: 1984
Rarity: D

HN2917 Legolas
Modelled by David Lyttleton
Height: 6 inches 15 cm
Introduced: 1981   Withdrawn: 1984
Rarity: D

HN2918 Boromir
Modelled by David Lyttleton
Height: 6$\frac{1}{4}$ inches 16 cm
Introduced: 1981   Withdrawn: 1984
Rarity: D

HN2922 Gimli
Modelled by David Lyttleton
Height: 5$\frac{1}{2}$ inches 13.5 cm
Introduced: 1981   Withdrawn: 1984
Rarity: D

HN2923 Barliman Butterbur
Modelled by David Lyttleton
Height: 5$\frac{1}{4}$ inches 13 cm
Introduced: 1982   Withdrawn: 1984
Rarity: C

HN2924 Tom Bombadil
Modelled by David Lyttleton
Height: 5$\frac{3}{4}$ inches 14.5 cm
Introduced: 1982   Withdrawn: 1984
Rarity: C

HN2925 Samwise
Modelled by David Lyttleton
Height: 4$\frac{1}{2}$ inches 11.5 cm
Introduced: 1982   Withdrawn: 1984
Rarity: C

NODDY AND BIG EARS

Royal Doulton backstamp

3676   **Big Ears**
Modelled by Andy Moss
Height: 5$\frac{1}{4}$ inches 13 cm
Introduced: 1997
Commissioned by
UK International Ceramics
in a limited edition of 1,500

3678   **Noddy**
Modelled by Andy Moss
Height: 5 inches 12.5 cm
Introduced: 1997
Commissioned by
UK International Ceramics
in a limited edition of 1,500

3769   **Mr Plod**
Modelled by Andy Moss
Introduced: 1998
Commissioned by
UK International Ceramics
in a limited edition of 1,500

3770   **Tessie Bear**
Modelled by Andy Moss
Introduced: 1998
Commissioned by
UK International Ceramics
in a limited edition of 1,500

PADDINGTON BEAR

Resin figures
Royal Doulton backstamp

PB1   **Paddington at the Station**
Modelled by Valerie Annand
Height: 4$\frac{1}{4}$ inches 10.5 cm
Introduced: 1996   Still in production
Rarity: F

PB2   **Paddington Bakes a Cake**
Modelled by Valerie Annand
Height: 4$\frac{1}{4}$ inches 10.5 cm
Introduced: 1996   Still in production
Rarity: F

PB3   **Paddington Decorating**
Modelled by Valerie Annand
Height: 4$\frac{3}{4}$ inches 12 cm
Introduced: 1996   Still in production
Rarity: F

PB4   **Paddington Surfing**
Modelled by Valerie Annand
Height: 4 inches 10 cm
Introduced: 1996   Still in production
Rarity: F

PB5   **Paddington Gardening**
Modelled by Valerie Annand
Height: 4 inches 10 cm
Introduced: 1996   Still in production
Rarity: F

Rarity Guide

PB6 **Paddington Bathtime**
Modelled by Valerie Annand
Height: 3¹/₂ inches 8.5 cm
Introduced: 1996   Still in production
Rarity: F

PB7 **Paddington the Golfer**
Modelled by Valerie Annand
Height: 3³/₄ inches 9.5 cm
Introduced: 1996   Still in production
Rarity: F

PB8 **Paddington the Musician**
Modelled by Valerie Annand
Height: 3³/₄ inches 9.5 cm
Introduced: 1996   Still in production
Rarity: F

PB9 **Paddington at Christmas Time**
Modelled by Valerie Annand
Height: 3¹/₂ inches 8.5 cm
Introduced: 1996   Still in production
Rarity: F

PB10 **Marmalade Sandwiches**
Modelled by Valerie Annand
Height: 3¹/₂ inches 8.5 cm
Introduced: 1997   Still in production
Rarity: F

PB11 **Going to Bed**
Modelled by Valerie Annand
Height: 3³/₄ inches 9 cm
Introduced: 1997   Still in production
Rarity: F

PB12 **Paddington the Fisherman**
Modelled by Valerie Annand
Height: 3¹/₂ inches 8.5 cm
Introduced: 1997   Still in production
Rarity: F

PIP, SQUEAK AND WILFRED

Royal Doulton backstamp
Designed by A B Payne for *The Daily Mirror*
newspaper

HN922 **Wilfred the Rabbit**
Height: 4 inches 10 cm
Introduced: 1927   Withdrawn: 1936
Rarity: B

HN935 **Pip, Squeak and Wilfred on Tray**
Height: 4 inches 10 cm
Introduced: 1927   Withdrawn: 1936
Rarity: A

RUPERT BEAR

John Beswick backstamp
Designed by Harry Sales

2694 **Rupert Bear**
Modelled by Graham Tongue
Height: 4¹/₄ inches 10.5 cm
Introduced: 1982   Withdrawn: 1985
Rarity: B

2710 **Algy Pug**
Modelled by Graham Tongue
Height: 4 inches 10 cm
Introduced: 1982   Withdrawn: 1985
Rarity: B

2711 **Pong Ping**
Modelled by Graham Tongue
Height: 4¹/₄ inches 10.5 cm
Introduced: 1982   Withdrawn: 1985
Rarity: B

2720 **Bill Badger**
Modelled by Graham Tongue
Height: 2³/₄ inches 7 cm
Introduced: 1982   Withdrawn: 1985
Rarity: B

2779 **Rupert Bear Snowballing**
Modelled by Graham Tongue
Height: 4¹/₄ inches 10.5 cm
Introduced: 1982   Withdrawn: 1985
Rarity: B

THE SNOWMAN

Royal Doulton backstamp
Designed by Harry Sales

DS1 **James**
Modelled by David Lyttleton
Height: 3³/₄ inches 9.5 cm
Introduced: 1985   Withdrawn: 1993
Rarity: C

DS2 **The Snowman**
Modelled by David Lyttleton
Height: 5 inches 12.5 cm
Introduced: 1985   Withdrawn: 1994
Rarity: D

DS3 **Stylish Snowman**
Modelled by David Lyttleton
Height: 5 inches 12.5 cm
Introduced: 1985   Withdrawn: 1993
Rarity: C

DS4 **Thank You Snowman**
Modelled by David Lyttleton
Height: 5 inches 12.5 cm
Introduced: 1985   Withdrawn: 1994
Rarity: D

DS5 Snowman Magic Musical Box
This features the figure DS2
and plays 'Walking in the Air'
Height: 8 inches 20.5 cm
Introduced: 1985   Withdrawn: 1994
Rarity: D

DS6 Cowboy Snowman
Modelled by David Lyttleton
Height: 5 inches 12.5 cm
Introduced: 1986   Withdrawn: 1992
Rarity: C

DS7 Highland Snowman
Modelled by David Lyttleton
Height: 5 inches 12.5 cm
Introduced: 1986   Withdrawn: 1993
Rarity: C

DS8 Lady Snowman
Modelled by David Lyttleton
Height: 5 inches 12.5 cm
Introduced: 1986   Withdrawn: 1992
Rarity: C

Designed by Graham Tongue

DS9 Bass Drummer Snowman
Modelled by Warren Platt
Height: 5½ inches 13.5 cm
Introduced: 1987   Withdrawn: 1993
Rarity: C

DS10 Flautist Snowman
Modelled by Warren Platt
Height: 5½ inches 13.5 cm
Introduced: 1987   Withdrawn: 1993
Rarity: C

DS11 Violinist Snowman
Modelled by Warren Platt
Height: 5¼ inches 13 cm
Introduced: 1987   Withdrawn: 1994
Rarity: D

DS12 Pianist Snowman
Modelled by Warren Platt
Height: 5 inches 12.5 cm
Introduced: 1987   Withdrawn: 1994
Rarity: D

DS13 Snowman's Piano
Modelled by Warren Platt
Height: 5 inches 12.5 cm
Introduced: 1997   Withdrawn: 1994
Rarity: D

DS14 Cymbal Player Snowman
Modelled by Warren Platt
Height: 5¼ inches 13 cm
Introduced: 1988   Withdrawn: 1993
Rarity: C

DS15 Drummer Snowman
Modelled by Warren Platt
Height: 5¾ inches 14.5 cm
Introduced: 1988   Withdrawn: 1994
Rarity: D

DS16 Trumpeter Snowman
Modelled by Warren Platt
Height: 5 inches 12.5 cm
Introduced: 1988   Withdrawn: 1993
Rarity: C

DS17 Cellist Snowman
Modelled by Warren Platt
Height: 5¼ inches 13 cm
Introduced: 1988   Withdrawn: 1993
Rarity: D

DS18 Snowman Musical Box
This features the figure DS7
and plays 'Blue Bells of Scotland'
Height: 8 inches 20.5 cm
Introduced: 1988   Withdrawn: 1990
Rarity: C

DS19 The Snowman Money Box
Modelled by Graham Tongue
Height: 8½ inches 21.5 cm
Introduced: 1990   Withdrawn: 1994
Rarity: D

DS20 The Snowman Tobogganing
Modelled by Warren Platt
Height: 5 inches 12.5 cm
Introduced: 1990   Withdrawn: 1994
Rarity: D

DS21 The Snowman Skiing
Modelled by Warren Platt
Height: 5 inches 12.5 cm
Introduced: 1990   Withdrawn: 1991
Rarity: B

DS22 The Snowballing Snowman
Modelled by Warren Platt
Height: 5 inches 12.5 cm
Introduced: 1990   Withdrawn: 1994
Rarity: D

DS23 Building the Snowman
Modelled by Warren Platt
Height: 4 inches 10 cm
Introduced: 1990   Withdrawn: 1994
Rarity: D

**D6972 The Snowman Character Jug
(Version 1)**
Modelled by Martyn Alcock
Height: 2¾ inches 7 cm
Introduced: 1994 only exclusively
for the USA
Rarity: D

**D7062 The Snowman Character Jug
(Version 2)**
Modelled by Bill Harper
Height: 2½ inches 6.5 cm
Introduced: 1997 Commissioned by
John Sinclair in a limited edition
of 2,000
Rarity: E

Rarity Guide

THELWELL

John Beswick backstamp
Designed by Harry Sales

2704G **An Angel on Horseback** (Grey)
Modelled by David Lyttleton
Height: 4½ inches 11.5 cm
Introduced: 1982   Withdrawn: 1989
Rarity: D

2704B **An Angel on Horseback** (Bay)
Modelled by David Lyttleton
Height: 4½ inches 11.5 cm
Introduced: 1982   Withdrawn: 1989
Rarity: D

2769G **Kick Start** (Grey)
Modelled by David Lyttleton
Height: 3½ inches 8.5 cm
Introduced: 1983   Withdrawn: 1989
Rarity: D

2769B **Kick Start** (Bay)
Modelled by David Lyttleton
Height: 3½ inches 8.5 cm
Introduced: 1983   Withdrawn: 1989
Rarity: D

2789G **Pony Express** (Grey)
Modelled by David Lyttleton
Height: 4½ inches 11.5 cm
Introduced: 1983   Withdrawn: 1989
Rarity: D

2798B **Pony Express** (Bay)
Modelled by David Lyttleton
Height: 4½ inches 11.5 cm
Introduced: 1983   Withdrawn: 1989
Rarity: D

Resin models in Studio Sculptures Series

John Beswick adhesive label
Designed by Harry Sales

SS7 **I Forgive You** (Grey)
Modelled by David Lyttleton
Height: 4 inches 10 cm
Introduced: 1984   Withdrawn: 1986
Rarity: C

I Forgive You (Bay)
Rarity:

SS12 **Early Bath** (Grey)
Modelled by David Lyttleton
Height: 4¾ inches 12 cm
Introduced: 1984   Withdrawn: 1986
Rarity: C

Early Bath (Bay)
Rarity: C

THUNDERBIRDS

John Beswick backstamp

3337 **Lady Penelope Bust**
Modelled by Bill Harper
Height: 4 inches 10 cm
Introduced: 1992
Commissioned by Lawleys by Post
in a limited edition of 2,500
Rarity: C

3339 **Brains Bust**
Modelled by Bill Harper
Height: 4 inches 10 cm
Introduced: 1992
Commissioned by Lawleys by Post
in a limited edition of 2,500
Rarity: C

3344 **Scott Tracy Bust**
Modelled by Bill Harper
Height: 4 inches 10 cm
Introduced: 1992
Commissioned by Lawleys by Post
in a limited edition of 2,500
Rarity: C

3345 **Virgil Tracy Bust**
Modelled by Bill Harper
Height: 4 inches 10 cm
Introduced: 1992
Commissioned by Lawleys by Post
in a limited edition of 2,500
Rarity: C

3346 **Parker Bust**
Modelled by Bill Harper
Height: 4 inches 10 cm
Introduced: 1992
Commissioned by Lawleys by Post
in a limited edition of 2,500
Rarity: C

3348 **The Hood Bust**
Modelled by Bill Harper
Height: 4 inches 10 cm
Introduced: 1992
Commissioned by Lawleys by Post
in a limited edition of 2,500
Rarity: C

TOM & JERRY

John Beswick backstamp

3552 **Tom**
Modelled by Simon Ward
Height: 4½ inches 11.5 cm
Introduced: 1995
Commissioned by
UK International Ceramics
in a limited edition of 2,000

3547   Jerry
Modelled by Simon Ward
Height: 3¼ inches 8 cm
Introduced: 1995
Commissioned by
UK International Ceramics
in a limited edition of 2,000

TOP CAT

John Beswick backstamp

3581   Top Cat
Modelled by Andy Moss
Height: 4½ inches 11.5 cm
Introduced: 1996
Commissioned for Doulton Fairs in
the UK in a limited edition of 2,000

3586   Choo-Choo
Modelled by Andy Moss
Height: 4½ inches 11.5 cm
Introduced: 1996
Commissioned for Doulton Fairs in
the UK in a limited edition of 2,000

3624   Fancy Fancy
Modelled by Andy Moss
Height: 4½ inches 11.5 cm
Introduced: 1997
Commissioned for Doulton Fairs in
the UK in a limited edition of 2,000

3627   Benny
Modelled by Andy Moss
Height: 3½ inches 8.5 cm
Introduced: 1997
Commissioned for Doulton Fairs in
the UK in a limited edition of 2,000

3671   Officer Dibble
Modelled by Andy Moss
Height: 7 inches 17.5 cm
Introduced: 1998
Commissioned for Doulton Fairs in
the UK in a limited edition of 2,000

3673   Spook
Modelled by Andy Moss
Height: 4½ inches 11.5 cm
Introduced: 1998
Commissioned for Doulton Fairs in
the UK in a limited edition of 2,000

3674   Brain
Modelled by Andy Moss
Height: 4 inches 10 cm
Introduced: 1998
Commissioned for Doulton Fairs in
the UK in a limited edition of 2,000

WALT DISNEY

Mickey and Friends

John Beswick backstamp

1278   Mickey Mouse
Modelled by Jan Granoska
Height: 4 inches 10 cm
Introduced: 1954   Withdrawn: 1965
Rarity: A

1280   Pluto
Modelled by Jan Granoska
Height: 3½ inches 8.5 cm
Introduced: 1954   Withdrawn: 1965
Rarity: A

1281   Goofy
Modelled by Jan Granoska
Height: 4¼ inches 11.5 cm
Introduced: 1954   Withdrawn: 1965
Rarity: A

1283   Donald Duck
Modelled by Jan Granoska
Height: 4 inches 10 cm
Introduced: 1954   Withdrawn: 1965
Rarity: A

1289   Minnie Mouse
Modelled by Jan Granoska
Height: 4 inches 10 cm
Introduced: 1954   Withdrawn: 1965
Rarity: A

Pinocchio

John Beswick backstamp

1279   Jiminy Cricket
Modelled by Jan Granoska
Height: 4 inches 10 cm
Introduced: 1954   Withdrawn: 1965
Rarity: A

1282   Pinocchio
Modelled by Jan Granoska
Height: 4 inches 10 cm
Introduced: 1954   Withdrawn: 1965
Rarity: A

Bambi

John Beswick backstamp

1291   Thumper
Modelled by Jan Granoska
Height: 3¾ inches 9.5 cm
Introduced: 1954   Withdrawn: 1965
Rarity: B

Rarity Guide

Peter Pan

John Beswick backstamp

1301 **Nana**
Modelled by Jan Granoska
Height: 3¼ inches 8 cm
Introduced: 1954 Withdrawn: 1965
Rarity: A

1302 **Smee**
Modelled by Jan Granoska
Height: 4¼ inches 10 cm
Introduced: 1954 Withdrawn: 1965
Rarity: A

1307 **Peter Pan**
Modelled by Jan Granoska
Height: 5 inches 12.5 cm
Introduced: 1954 Withdrawn: 1965
Rarity: A

1312 **Tinker Bell**
Modelled by Jan Granoska
Height: 5 inches 12.5 cm
Introduced: 1954 Withdrawn: 1965
Rarity: A

Snow White

First Series

John Beswick backstamp

1325 **Dopey**
Modelled by Arthur Gredington
Height: 3½ inches 8.5 cm
Introduced: 1955 Withdrawn: 1967
Rarity: B

1326 **Happy**
Modelled by Arthur Gredington
Height: 3½ inches 8.5 cm
Introduced: 1955 Withdrawn: 1967
Rarity: B

1327 **Bashful**
Modelled by Arthur Gredington
Height: 3½ inches 8.5 cm
Introduced: 1955 Withdrawn: 1967
Rarity: B

1328 **Sneezy**
Modelled by Arthur Gredington
Height: 3½ inches 8.5 cm
Introduced: 1955 Withdrawn: 1967
Rarity: B

1329 **Doc**
Modelled by Arthur Gredington
Height: 3½ inches 8.5 cm
Introduced: 1955 Withdrawn: 1967
Rarity: B

1330 **Grumpy**
Modelled by Arthur Gredington
Height: 3½ inches 8.5 cm
Introduced: 1955 Withdrawn: 1967
Rarity: B

1331 **Sleepy**
Modelled by Arthur Gredington
Height: 3½ inches 8.5 cm
Introduced: 1955 Withdrawn: 1967
Rarity: B

1332 **Snow White**
Modelled by Arthur Gredington
Height: 5 inches 12.5 cm
Introduced: 1955 Withdrawn: 1967
Rarity: B

Second Series

Royal Doulton backstamp

SW1 **Snow White**
Modelled by Amanda Hughes-Lubeck
Height: 5¾ inches 14.5 cm
Introduced in 1997 in a limited
edition of 2,000 and issued in 1998 in
an unlimited edition with a different
backstamp
Rarity: F

SW2 **Doc**
Modelled by Amanda Hughes-Lubeck
Height: 3¼ inches 8 cm
Introduced in 1997 in a limited
edition of 2,000 and issued in 1998 in
an unlimited edition with a different
backstamp
Rarity: F

SW3 **Grumpy**
Modelled by Shane Ridge
Height: 3½ inches 8.5 cm
Introduced in 1997 in a limited
edition of 2,000 and issued in 1998 in
an unlimited edition with a different
backstamp
Rarity: F

SW4 **Happy**
Modelled by Amanda Hughes-Lubeck
Height: 3¾ inches 9.5 cm
Introduced in 1997 in a limited
edition of 2,000 and issued in 1998 in
an unlimited edition with a different
backstamp
Rarity: F

SW5 **Dopey**
Modelled by Shane Ridge
Height: 3½ inches 8.5 cm
Introduced in 1997 in a limited
edition of 2,000 and issued in 1998 in
an unlimited edition with a different
backstamp
Rarity: F

SW6   Sneezy
Modelled by Warren Platt
Height: 3½ inches 8.5 cm
Introduced in 1997 in a limited
edition of 2,000 and issued in 1998 in
an unlimited edition with a different
backstamp
Rarity: F

SW7   Sleepy
Modelled by Warren Platt
Height: 3½ inches 8.5 cm
Introduced in 1997 in a limited
edition of 2,000 and issued in 1998 in
an unlimited edition with a different
backstamp
Rarity: F

SW8   Bashful
Modelled by Amanda Hughes-Lubeck
Height: 3½ inches 8.5 cm
Introduced in 1997 in a limited
edition of 2,000 and issued in 1998 in
an unlimited edition with a different
backstamp
Rarity: F

Princess Collection

Royal Doulton backstamp

HN3677 Cinderella
from *Cinderella*
Modelled by Pauline Parsons
Height: 8 inches 20.5 cm
Introduced: 1995
Commissioned by Disney
in a limited edition of 2,000

HN3678 Snow White
from *Snow White*
Modelled by Pauline Parsons
Height: 8 inches 20.5 cm
Introduced: 1995
Commissioned by Disney
in a limited edition of 2,000

HN3830 Belle
from *Beauty and the Beast*
Modelled by Pauline Parsons
Height: 8 inches 20.5 cm
Introduced: 1996
Commissioned by Disney
in a limited edition of 2,000

HN3831 Ariel
from *The Little Mermaid*
Modelled by Pauline Parsons
Height: 8 inches 20.5 cm
Introduced: 1996
Commissioned by Disney
in a limited edition of 2,000

HN3832 Jasmine
from *Aladdin*
Modelled by Pauline Parsons
Height: 8 inches 20.5 cm
Introduced: 1996
Commissioned by Disney
in a limited edition of 2,000

HN3833 Aurora
from *Sleeping Beauty*
Modelled by Pauline Parsons
Height: 8 inches 20.5 cm
Introduced: 1996
Commissioned by Disney
in a limited edition of 2,000

Villains Collection
Royal Doulton backstamp

HN3839 Cruella de Vil
from *101 Dalmatians*
Modelled by Pauline Parsons
Height: 8 inches 20.5 cm
Introduced: 1998
Commissioned by Disney
in a limited edition of 2,000

HN3840 Maleficent
from *Sleeping Beauty*
Modelled by Pauline Parsons
Height: 8 inches 20.5 cm
Introduced: 1998
Commissioned by Disney
in a limited edition of 2,000

101 Dalmatians
Royal Doulton backstamp

DM1   Cruella de Vil
Modelled by Martyn Alcock
Height: 6¼ inches 16 cm
Introduced: 1997   Still in production
Rarity: F

DM2   Penny
Modelled by Shane Ridge
Height: 2¾ inches 7 cm
Introduced: 1997   Still in production
Rarity: F

DM3   Penny and Freckles
Modelled by Shane Ridge
Height: 2¼ inches 5.5 cm
Introduced: 1997   Still in production
Rarity: F

DM4   Rolly
Modelled by Shane Ridge
Height: 2¾ inches 7 cm
Introduced: 1997   Still in production
Rarity: F

DM5   Patch, Rolly and Freckles
Modelled by Shane Ridge
Height: 3¾ inches 9.5 cm
Introduced in 1997 in a limited
edition of 3,500

Rarity Guide

DM6 **Pongo**
Modelled by Shane Ridge
Height: 4^1/$_2$ inches 11.5 cm
Introduced: 1997   Still in production
Rarity: F

DM7 **Perdita**
Modelled by Martyn Alcock
Height: 2^1/$_2$ inches 6.5 cm
Introduced: 1997   Still in production
Rarity: F

DM8 **Lucky**
Modelled by Martyn Alcock
Height: 2^3/$_4$ inches 7 cm
Introduced: 1997   Still in production
Rarity: F

WIND IN THE WILLOWS

Royal Albert backstamp
Designed by Harry Sales

2939 **Mole**
Modelled by David Lyttleton
Height: 3 inches 7.5 cm
Introduced: 1987   Withdrawn: 1989
Rarity: C

2940 **Badger**
Modelled by David Lyttleton
Height: 3 inches 7.5 cm
Introduced: 1987   Withdrawn: 1989
Rarity: C

2941 **Ratty**
Modelled by David Lyttleton
Height: 3^3/$_4$ inches 9.5 cm
Introduced: 1987   Withdrawn: 1989
Rarity: C

2942 **Toad**
Modelled by David Lyttleton
Height: 3^3/$_4$ inches 9.5 cm
Introduced: 1987   Withdrawn: 1989
Rarity: C

3065 **Portly**
Modelled by Alan Maslankowski
Height: 2^3/$_4$ inches 7 cm
Introduced: 1988   Withdrawn: 1989
Rarity: B

3076 **Weasel**
Modelled by Alan Maslankowski
Height: 4 inches 10 cm
Introduced: 1988   Withdrawn: 1989
Rarity: B

WINNIE THE POOH

First Series

John Beswick backstamp
Designed by Harry Sales

2193 **Winnie the Pooh**
Modelled by Albert Hallam
Height: 2^1/$_2$ inches 6.5 cm
Introduced: 1969   Withdrawn: 1989
Rarity: D

2196 **Eeyore**
Modelled by Albert Hallam
Height: 2 inches 5.5 cm
Introduced: 1969   Withdrawn: 1989
Rarity: D

2214 **Piglet**
Modelled by Albert Hallam
Height: 2^3/$_4$ inches 7 cm
Introduced: 1969   Withdrawn: 1989
Rarity: D

2215 **Rabbit**
Modelled by Albert Hallam
Height: 3 inches 7.5 cm
Introduced: 1969   Withdrawn: 1989
Rarity: D

2216 **Owl**
Modelled by Albert Hallam
Height: 3 inches 7.5 cm
Introduced: 1969   Withdrawn: 1989
Rarity: D

2217 **Kanga**
Modelled by Albert Hallam
Height: 3 inches 7.5 cm
Introduced: 1969   Withdrawn: 1989
Rarity: D

2394 **Tigger**
Modelled by Graham Tongue
Height: 3 inches 7.5 cm
Introduced: 1972   Withdrawn: 1989
Rarity: C

2395 **Christopher Robin**
Modelled by Graham Tongue
Height: 4^3/$_4$ inches 12 cm
Introduced: 1972   Withdrawn: 1989
Rarity: C

Second Series

Royal Doulton backstamp
A special commemorative mark was used in
1996 only

WP1 **Winnie the Pooh and the Honey Pot**
Modelled by Warren Platt
Height: 2^1/$_2$ inches 6.5 cm
Introduced: 1996   Still in production
Rarity: F

WP2 **Pooh and Piglet — The Windy Day**
Modelled by Martyn Alcock
Height: 3½ inches 8.5 cm
Introduced: 1996   Still in production
Rarity: F

WP3 **Winnie the Pooh and the Paw Marks**
Modelled by Warren Platt
Height: 2¾ inches 7 cm
Introduced: 1996   Withdrawn: 1997
Rarity: E

WP4 **Winnie the Pooh in the Armchair**
Modelled by Shane Ridge
Height: 3½ inches 8.5 cm
Introduced: 1996   Still in production
Rarity: F

WP5 **Piglet and Balloon**
Modelled by Warren Platt
Height: 2¾ inches 7 cm
Introduced: 1996   Still in production
Rarity: F

WP6 **Tigger Signs the Risolution**
Modelled by Martyn Alcock
Height: 1¾ inches 4.5 cm
Introduced: 1996   Still in production
Rarity: F

WP7 **Eeyore's Tail**
Modelled by Shane Ridge
Height: 3½ inches 8.5 cm
Introduced: 1996   Still in production
Rarity: F

WP8 **Kanga and Roo**
Modelled by Martyn Alcock
Height: 3¾ inches 9.5 cm
Introduced: 1996   Still in production
Rarity: F

WP9 **Christopher Robin**
Modelled by Shane Ridge
Height: 5½ inches 13.5 cm
Introduced: 1996   Still in production
Rarity: F

WP10 **Christopher Robin and Pooh**
Modelled by Shane Ridge
Height: 3½ inches 8.5 cm
Introduced: 1996   Withdrawn: 1997
Rarity: E

WP11 **Pooh Lights the Candle**
Modelled by Graham Tongue
Height: 3¾ inches 9.5 cm
Introduced: 1997   Still in production
Rarity: F

WP12 **Pooh Counting the Honeypots**
Modelled by Martyn Alcock
Height: 3¾ inches 9.5 cm
Introduced: 1997   Still in production
Rarity: F

WP13 **Piglet Picking the Violets**
Modelled by Graham Tongue
Height: 2½ inches 6.5 cm
Introduced: 1997   Still in production
Rarity: F

WP14 **Eeyore's Birthday**
Modelled by Martyn Alcock
Height: 2¾ inches 7 cm
Introduced: 1997   Still in production
Rarity: F

WP15 **Eeyore Loses a Tail**
Modelled by Martyn Alcock
Height: 4 inches 10 cm
Introduced: 1997 in a limited edition
of 5,000
Rarity: D

WP16 **Pooh's Blue Balloon Money Ball**
Modelled by Shane Ridge
Height: 4¼ inches 10.5 cm
Introduced: 1997   Still in production
Rarity: F

WIZARD OF OZ

Royal Doulton backstamp

3709 **Scarecrow**
Modelled by Andy Moss
Height: 6½ inches 16.5 cm
Introduced: 1998
Commissioned by
UK International Ceramics
in a limited edition of 1,500

3731 **Lion**
Modelled by Andy Moss
Height: 6 inches 15 cm
Introduced: 1998
Commissioned by
UK International Ceramics
in a limited edition of 1,500

3732 **Dorothy**
Modelled by Andy Moss
Height: 5 inches 12.5 cm
Introduced: 1998
Commissioned by
UK International Ceramics
in a limited edition of 1,500

3738 **Tinman**
Modelled by Andy Moss
Height: 7 inches 17.5 cm
Introduced: 1998
Commissioned by
UK International Ceramics
in a limited edition of 1,500

In the Marketplace

NICK TZIMAS

WHERE TO BUY

Current cartoon figures are available from specialist china and gift shops in many parts of the world. Details of stockists and other product information can be obtained from one of Royal Doulton's Distribution and Sales Companies.

Royal Doulton
Sales Division
Minton House, London Road
Stoke-on Trent ST4 7QD
England

Royal Doulton USA INC.
700 Cottontail Lane
Somerset
NJ 08873, USA

Royal Doulton Canada Ltd
850 Progress Avenue
Scarborough
Ontario M1H 3C4, Canada

Royal Doulton Australia Pty Ltd
17-23 Merriwa Street, Gordon
NSW 2072, Australia

Royal Doulton Europe
Europark Noord 25
B-9100 Sint Niklaas
Belgium

Royal Doulton Dodwell Ltd
No. 35 Kowa Building
14-14 Akasaka
1-Chome, Minato-Ku
Tokyo 107
Japan

Details of **UK International Ceramics** Special Exclusive Commissions can be obtained by writing to:

Zoë Gilligan, Product Executive, UKI Ceramics Ltd
10 Wilford Bridge Spur, Melton, Woodbridge, Suffolk, England
IP12 1RJ. Tel: 01394 386662. Fax: 01394 386742.

Details of **John Sinclair** Special Exclusive Commissions can be obtained by writing to:

Mrs Irene Harrison, Mail Order Manager, John Sinclair
266 Glossop Road, Sheffield S10 2HS
Tel: 0114 2750 333. Fax: 0114 2754 443.

Discontinued figures can be purchased from antique shops, markets and fairs as well as some auction houses. There are specialist dealers who attend the venues and events below but it is also worth browsing at general shops and stalls as well as country auctions.

UK

New Caledonian Market
Bermondsey Square
London SE1
Friday morning
(Nearest tube London Bridge)

Portobello Road Market
London W11
Saturday only
(Nearest tube Notting Hill Gate)

Alfie's Antique Market
13-25 Church Street
London NW8
Tuesday-Saturday
(Nearest tube Edgware Road)

Camden Passage Market
off Upper Street
London N1
Wednesday and Saturday
(Nearest tube Angel)

Louis Taylor Auction House
10 Town Road, Hanley
Stoke-on-Trent ST1 2QG

Peter Wilson Auction House
Victoria Gallery
Market Street
Nantwich, Cheshire

Potteries Antique Centre Auction
271 Waterloo Road, Cobridge
Stoke on Trent ST6 3HR

Phillips Auction House
101 New Bond Street
London W1Y 0AS

Christies South Kensington
85 Old Brompton Road
London SW7 3LD

Bonhams Chelsea
65-69 Lots Road
London SW10 0RN

Sothebys Auction House
Summers Place
Billingshurst
West Sussex RH14 9AD

The UK Doulton & Beswick Fair for Collectors
The Queensway Hall, Civic Centre
Dunstable
Bedfordshire
Enquiries: 01394 386663

Trentham Gardens International Doulton Fair
Trentham, Stoke on Trent
Enquiries: 0114 2750333

Doulton & Beswick Collectors Fair
The National Motorcycle Museum
Birmingham
Enquiries: 0181 3033316

Alexandra Palace Collectors Fairs
Wood Green
London N22 4AM
(various dates — see local press)

USA

Information about general shows and markets can be found in the local press and specialist publications such as *The Antique Trader Weekly*. For Doulton and Beswick shows enquire from the following list of specialist dealers who also stock Doulton and Beswick cartoon figures.

Curio Cabinet
679 High Street
Worthington
Ohio 43085
Tel: (614) 885 1986

Colonial House Antiques
182 Front Street
Berea
Ohio 44017
Tel: (216) 826 4169

Charles Dombeck
9552 N.W. 9th Court
Plantation
FL 33324
Tel: (305) 452 9174

Seaway China Company
102 Broadway
Marine City
MI 48039
Tel: (313) 765 9000

Pascoe & Co
101 Almeria Avenue
Coral Gables
FL 33134
Tel: (305) 445 3229

CANADA

Canadian Art and Collectibles Show
Kitchener Memorial Auditorium
400 East Avenue, Kitchener
Ontario
Enquiries: (519) 364 3217

Information about general fairs and markets can be found in the local press and specialist publications such as *Antique Showcase*.

The following china retailers also stock cartoon figures:

Ian Campbell
Site of The Green
RR # 1 Dundas
Ontario L9H 5E1
Tel: (905) 627 1304

George Bagnall
166 Royalty Road
Winsloe RR # 2
P.E.I C1E 1Z4
Tel: (902) 368 1212

AUSTRALIA AND NEW ZEALAND

Various general antique fairs and markets are held throughout both countries and information can be found in the local press and specialist publications such as *Carter's Australian Antique Trader*.

The following china retailers also stock cartoon figures:

Alma Foster
Thorndon Antiques
PO Box 12-076
Wellington
New Zealand
Tel: (04) 473 0173

Ray James Ltd
3 Burns Street
Grey Lynn
Auckland 2
New Zealand
Tel: (09) 376 3402

Pam Shannon
Antiques International
Shop 15
Brisbane Antique Market
789 Sandgate Road
Clayfield QLD 4011
Tel: (617) 3862 4640

Bayside Antiques
123 Herald Street
Cheltenham
Australia 3192
Tel: (613) 9555 7011

PLACES TO VISIT

Take a tour of the Beswick factory to see cartoon figures being made:

John Beswick
Gold Street
Longton
Stoke-on-Trent ST3 2JP
For opening times and tour information telephone (01782) 292292

A few discontinued cartoon figures are on display in Royal Doulton's own collection:

Sir Henry Doulton Gallery
Nile Street
Burslem
Stoke-on-Trent ST6 2AJ
For opening times telephone (01782) 292292

CLUBS AND MAGAZINES

The Royal Doulton International Collectors Club publishes **Gallery,** a quarterly magazine which gives information about new introductions and articles on historical pieces. The Club also commissions collectable products exclusively for members. For details of membership, contact the nearest Royal Doulton Distribution and Sales company — addresses on page 185.

Collecting Doulton is a subscription magazine about Doulton and Beswick wares past and present and it regularly includes features about cartoon figures. For further information contact:

Collecting Doulton
PO Box 310
Richmond
Surrey TW9 1FS

Further Reading

Beatrix Potter Figures and Gift Ware	Edited by Louise Irvine *UK International Ceramics Ltd* *Second Edition 1996*
Royal Doulton Bunnykins Figures	Louise Irvine *UK International Ceramics Ltd* *Third Edition 1996*
Royal Doulton Bunnykins Collectors Book	Louise Irvine *Richard Dennis Publications* *Revised Edition 1993*
Royal Doulton Series Ware Volume 3 'Doulton in the Nursery'	Louise Irvine *Richard Dennis Publications 1986*
John Beswick 'A World of Imagination' 1950 – 1996	Reprinted trade catalogues *UK International Ceramics Ltd* *Revised Edition 1996*
Gifts for Good Children Part II	Maureen Batkin *Richard Dennis Publications 1996*
The Charlton Standard Catalogue of Royal Doulton and Beswick Storybook Characters	Jean Dale *Charlton Press 1995*
Disneyana	Robert Heide and John Gilman *Hyperion 1994*
Bonzo	Paul Babb and Gay Owen *Richard Dennis Publications 1988*
Children's China	Pauline Flick *Constable and Co. 1983*

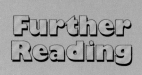

**Illustrated Encyclopedia of
Cartoon Animals**

Jeff Rovin
Prentice Hall Press 1991

Of Mice and Magic

Leonard Maltin
Plume 1987

**The Great Cartoon Stars
A Who's Who**

Dennis Gifford
Jupiter Books 1979

The International Book of Comics

Dennis Gifford
Hamlyn 1990

Penny Dreadfuls and Comics

Exhibition Catalogue
*Bethnal Green Museum of
Childhood 1983*

The Art of Hanna-Barbera

Ted Sennett
Viking 1989

Index of Character Illustrations

Index of Character Illustrations

Index of Character Illustrations

Index of Character Illustrations

Index of Character Illustrations

Collector's Notes

Collector's Notes

Collector's Notes

Collector's Notes

Collector's Notes

Collector's Notes

Collector's Notes